Created by
Marilyn Burns

Teacher Implementation Guide

Credits appear on page 2, which constitutes an extension of this copyright page.

Copyright © 2008 by Scholastic Inc.

All rights reserved.   Published by Scholastic Inc.   ·   Printed in the U.S.A.

ISBN-13: 978-0-545-07070-6
ISBN-10: 0-545-07070-8

SCHOLASTIC, DO THE MATH, WORKSPACE and associated logos and designs are trademarks and/or registered trademarks of Scholastic Inc. Other company names, brand names, and product names are the property and/or trademarks of their respective owners.

3 4 5 6 7 8 9 10   40   17 16 15 14 13 12 11

Bibliography

Baker, S., Gersten, R., Lee, D. S. (2002). "A Synthesis of Empirical Research on Teaching Mathematics to Low-Achieving Students." *The Elementary School Journal*, 103(1), 51–73.

Ball, D. L., Mundy, J. F., Kilpatrick, J., Milgram, R. J., Schmid, W., and Schaar, R. (2005). "Reaching for Common Ground in K–12 Mathematics Education." *Notices of the AMS*, 52(9), 1055–1058.

Chapin, S., O'Connor, C., and Anderson, N. C. (2003). *Classroom Discussions: Using Math Talk to Help Students Learn, Grades 1–6*. Sausalito, CA: Math Solutions Publications.

Gee, J. P. (2003). *What Video Games Have to Teach Us About Learning and Literacy*. New York: Palgrave/Macmillan.

Grouws, D. G., and Cebulla, K. J. (2000). "Improving Student Achievement in Mathematics. Part 1: Research Findings." *ERIC Clearinghouse for Science, Mathematics, and Environmental Education*. [Online]. Available: http://www.stemworks.org/digests/dse00-09.html

Lee, J., Grigg, W., and Dion, G. (2007). *The Nation's Report Card: Mathematics 2007* (NCES 2007-494). Washington, D.C.: National Center for Education Statistics, Institute of Education Sciences, U.S. Department of Education.

Marzano, R. J. (2002). "Language, the Language Arts, and Thinking." In J. Flood, D. Lapp, J. R. Squire, and J. M. Jensen (Eds.), *Handbook of Research on Teaching the English Language Arts, Second Edition*. Mahwah, NJ: Lawrence Erlbaum Associates, 687–716.

Mullis, I. V. S., Martin, M. O., Gonzalez, E. J., and Chrostowski, S. J. (2004). *TIMSS 2003 International Mathematics Report: Findings From IEA's Trends in International Mathematics and Science Study at the Fourth and Eighth Grades*. Boston, MA: TIMSS & PIRLS International Study Center, Lynch School of Education, Boston College.

Raiker, A. (2002). "Spoken Language and Mathematics." *Cambridge Journal of Education*, 32(1), 45–60.

Routman, R. (2003). *Reading Essentials: The Specifics You Need to Teach Reading Well*. Portsmouth, NH: Heinemann.

Witzel, B. S., Mercer, C. D., and Miller, D. M. (2003). "Teaching Algebra to Students with Learning Difficulties: An Investigation of an Explicit Instruction Model." *Learning Disabilities Research and Practice*, 18(2),121–131.

Credits

Contents

Dear *Do The Math* Educator,

Welcome to the *Do The Math* Implementation Training. This training will introduce you to this highly effective, teacher-tested arithmetic intervention program and provide you with strategies for successfully implementing *Do The Math* in your classroom.

Our nation's youth continue to struggle with high-level math because they have yet to achieve proficiency with whole numbers and fractions, both of which are critical foundations for algebra. *Do The Math* rebuilds critical math foundations, giving students who have fallen behind the chance to catch up and keep up.

Created by Marilyn Burns, along with a team of Math Solutions master classroom teachers, *Do The Math* offers teachers tools and resources to help struggling students reach grade level. Through the use of research-based and teacher-tested strategies, engaging teaching materials, and explicit step-by-step instruction, *Do The Math* helps students gain the conceptual understanding, computational proficiency, and problem-solving skills necessary to proceed successfully.

During this training, you will become familiar with the *Do The Math* program materials and the organization of the math modules. You will practice effective intervention strategies and learn how *Do The Math* differentiates instruction to meet the needs of individual students.

This *Teacher Implementation Guide* and the training today will provide you with an overall understanding of the program and the tools necessary to begin to implement *Do The Math*.

We thank you for your commitment to support struggling students as they develop the foundation of knowledge they need to be successful in math.

Sincerely,

Marilyn Trow

Marilyn Trow
Director of Educational Partnerships in Math
Scholastic Education

Do The Math
Implementation Training
Agenda

20 minutes   **Welcome and Program Background**

20 minutes   **Materials Overview**

30 minutes   ***Do The Math* Model Lesson**

                  Break

40 minutes   **Teaching With *Do The Math***

- Using the Teacher Guide
- Instructional Strategies

20 minutes   **Assessing and Differentiating Instruction**

- Summative Assessments
- Progress Monitoring

15 minutes   **Implementing *Do The Math***

10 minutes   **Ongoing Professional Development**

10 minutes   **Final Questions and Evaluation**

The Challenge

Although recent studies reveal some positive trends in math achievement, a high percentage of students in the U.S. are still struggling. Without proficiency in basic math concepts, these students will be ill-equipped to meet the future demands of college and the workplace.

2003 TIMSS Report

According to the 2003 Trends in International Mathematics and Science Study (TIMSS), American students are not achieving proficiency in math as compared to their counterparts in most other industrialized nations:

- U.S. fourth-grade students ranked 12th in overall mathematics achievement.
- U.S. eighth-grade students ranked 15th in the world.

2007 NAEP Results

Every two years, the National Assessment of Educational Progress (NAEP) releases the Nation's Report Card in Mathematics with the results of national assessments that evaluate students' understanding of math concepts and their ability to apply math in everyday situations. The most recent findings report an alarming number of students with basic and below-basic scores in mathematics. The results also indicate that significant and persistent disparities remain related to race, ethnicity, and income.

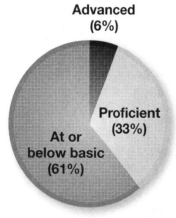

2007 NAEP Data, 4th Grade

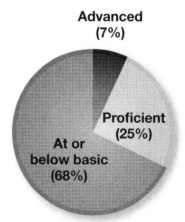

2007 NAEP Data, 8th Grade

 Reflecting on the Data

With the data in mind, how would you rate your district, school, and students?

_____

_____

_____

Barriers to Math Proficiency

Every teacher has students who struggle with math. Effective instruction can help break the barriers that keep students from achieving success.

Barriers for Struggling Students	*Do The Math* Intervention Solutions
Lack of number sense	
View of math as a series of isolated skills	
Weak foundation in math vocabulary	
Dislike of math	
Lack of foundational knowledge	
First language other than English	
Limited practice of math skills	
Lack of time to internalize learning	
Difficulty making connections	

Do The Math Philosophy

Do The Math is a program for students who are behind in math or struggling with grade-level content. The explicit instruction, manageable sections of content, deliberate pacing, and meaningful practice enable struggling students to develop proficiency with whole numbers and fractions.

The program adheres to this philosophy: all students are capable of success in math and all teachers can be effective math teachers if they have the right tools and materials.

All Students Can Be Proficient in Math

Do The Math focuses on number and operations, the cornerstone of elementary mathematics. Students become successful once they learn the basics of math—computation, number sense, and problem solving.

Do The Math helps students develop:

■ core skills necessary to compute with accuracy and efficiency.

■ number sense to reason effectively.

■ competence in applying these skills and reasoning to solve problems.

Do The Math helps students by:

■ focusing on conceptual understanding.

■ developing computational fluency.

■ building connections through a logical progression of scaffolded content.

All Teachers Can Be Effective Math Teachers

Do The Math includes the following tools that teachers need to help struggling math students become successful:

■ Well-developed lessons with clear objectives

■ Clear instructions for teachers and students

■ Integrated instructional support for classroom management

■ Built-in formative assessment and differentiated instruction

■ Resources for professional development

> 66 *Do The Math* is all about helping teachers support students who struggle. The program provides carefully planned and sequenced lessons to help build the mathematical understandings that students need for continued success. 99
>
> —Marilyn Burns

Meet Marilyn Burns

Marilyn Burns is one of the most highly respected mathematics educators in the United States today. For more than 40 years, Ms. Burns has educated children, conducted countless in-service workshops, published several children's books, and written numerous professional resources for teachers and administrators. In 1984, Ms. Burns founded Math Solutions Professional Development, an organization dedicated to the improvement of math instruction. She has received a number of accolades including the Glenn Gilbert National Leadership Award, given by the National Council of Supervisors of Mathematics, and the Louise Hay Award for Contributions to Mathematics Education, given by the Association for Women in Mathematics.

Marilyn Burns, along with a team of Math Solutions instructors with extensive experience, created the lessons in *Do The Math*. They discussed, wrote, debated, tested, rewrote, and refined the lessons to ensure that the content, pacing, and scaffolding were on target to meet the needs of struggling students.

> 66 Creating *Do The Math* has surprisingly and substantially changed my own teaching. My lessons have become more intentional, more focused, and more effective for helping all students have success with mathematics. 99
>
> —**Marilyn Burns**

Introducing *Do The Math*

Do The Math is organized into 12 modules. There are three modules in each of the topic areas: Addition & Subtraction, Multiplication, Division, and Fractions. Each module includes 30 lessons designed for 30-minute classes, five days a week.

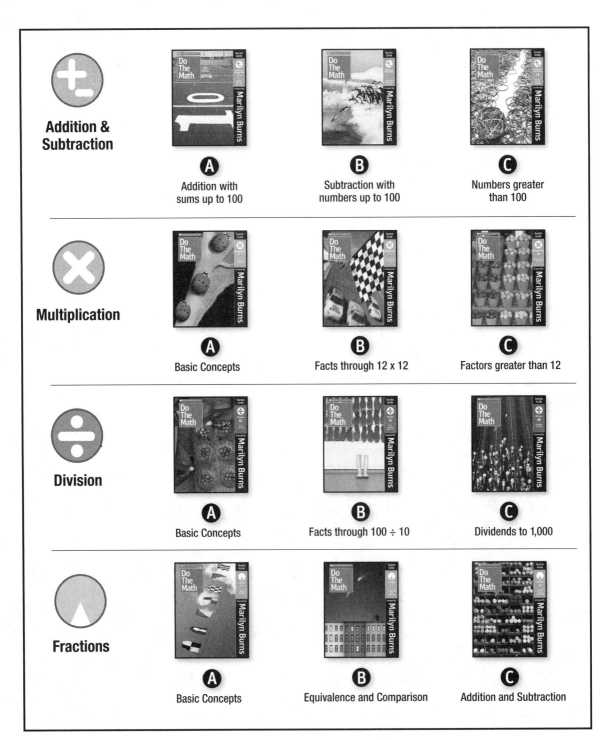

Addition & Subtraction

A — Addition with sums up to 100

B — Subtraction with numbers up to 100

C — Numbers greater than 100

Multiplication

A — Basic Concepts

B — Facts through 12 x 12

C — Factors greater than 12

Division

A — Basic Concepts

B — Facts through 100 ÷ 10

C — Dividends to 1,000

Fractions

A — Basic Concepts

B — Equivalence and Comparison

C — Addition and Subtraction

Do The Math Modules

Key Arithmetic Concepts and Skills

Each module of *Do The Math* scaffolds and paces key concepts and skills for students who struggle with math.

 Addition & Subtraction

- **Module A:** Add two-digit numbers to the sum of 100.

- **Module B:** Subtract from numbers up to 100.

- **Module C:** Develop computational strategies to add and subtract with numbers up to the 1,000s.

 Multiplication

- **Module A:** Understand the concept of multiplication.

- **Module B:** Learn multiplication facts up to 12 x 12 and use the multiplication table to understand those numbers.

- **Module C:** Develop the tools and strategies to multiply two two-digit numbers.

 Division

- **Module A:** Build understanding of the meaning of division and remainders.

- **Module B:** Continue learning with divisors up to 10 and dividends to 100.

- **Module C:** Build the computation tools and strategies to solve problems with larger numbers, including two-digit divisors.

 Fractions

- **Module A:** Build an understanding of fractions using a limited set of fractions. Identify equivalent fractions, compare and order fractions, and combine fractions with like denominators.

- **Module B:** Develop a tool kit of strategies to compare and order any fractions, including fractions greater than 1.

- **Module C:** Add and subtract fractions, including improper fractions and mixed numbers, with like and unlike denominators. Represent fractions in lowest terms or simplest form, and estimate sums or differences.

Getting to Know the Materials

One module of *Do The Math* includes materials for teacher instruction, professional support, and student practice.

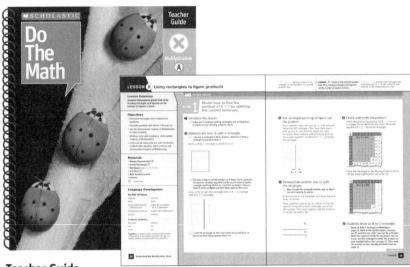

Teacher Bookcase

Stores all of the teaching materials and professional resources needed for one *Do The Math* module

Teacher Guide

Contains step-by-step teaching instructions, guidance for monitoring student progress, and information about how to use other program materials

TeacherSpace™

Includes a CD-ROM with videos, reproducibles, and professional articles

Annotated WorkSpace
Annotated version of the student *WorkSpace* with answers for quick progress monitoring

One module includes materials for up to eight students. Whole-class modules are also available for up to 24 students.

WorkSpace
(8 copies per module)
Assignments to support students' transition to independent work and to monitor progress

Teaching Arithmetic
A professional resource from Math Solutions Publications that provides mathematical and pedagogical support

Read Alouds
Two copies of one or two children's books to provide an engaging springboard for instruction

Student Pair Materials
(4 bags for 8 students)
Hands-on materials to support student learning

Teacher Demonstration Materials
One bag of demonstration materials to model instruction and games

Games
(1 bag for 8 students)
Materials for games that provide practice with math concepts and skills

Proven Instructional Strategies

The following research-based strategies that are proven to raise student achievement form the basis of *Do The Math* lessons.

Scaffolded Content

Scaffolding is a strategy of breaking challenging tasks or skills into manageable steps. Three strategies for scaffolding content—organization of concepts, sequencing, and chunking—support teaching for conceptual understanding (Grouws and Cebulla, 2000).

Do The Math presents essential content in small steps to support students in developing conceptual understanding and skills with number and operations. All of the lessons are carefully sequenced and paced so that students can be successful. Each section of new content connects to and builds upon previously learned content.

> 66 The program offers students multiple approaches to ideas in lessons that are paced slowly…and with the content scaffolded so the students build the foundations of understanding they need. 99
>
> —**Marilyn Burns**

Explicit Instruction

Students who struggle with math typically fail to make connections between math concepts. Explicit instruction is a proven pedagogical strategy for building mathematical knowledge (Witzel et al., 2003). During explicit instruction, teachers demonstrate and model how to complete a task, guide students in understanding and articulating relationships, and help students make connections between previous math experiences and newly acquired concepts.

The step-by-step lessons in *Do The Math* help students develop understanding, learn skills, see relationships, and make connections. Learning experiences link concepts and skills to their mathematical representations and language.

Multiple Strategies

Using multiple strategies to teach math concepts allows teachers to reach more students and strengthens conceptual understanding (Ball et al., 2005).

Do The Math lessons engage students with each concept and skill in multiple ways, deepening their knowledge.

- Manipulatives provide students with concrete experiences to support their understanding of abstract math concepts.
- Games engage students in interactive practice to reinforce mathematical understandings and skills.
- Children's literature provides a springboard for introducing new math concepts.
- Meaningful contexts help students access abstract math concepts.
- Visual representations help students connect to symbolic representations.

Gradual Release

Students achieve optimal learning when they move through phases of dependence to achieve independence. Through the guidance of a teacher using a gradual release of responsibility model of instruction, students learn to successfully apply newly acquired skills on their own (Routman, 2003).

The four-phase pedagogy in *Do The Math* prepares students for individual success.

Phase 1 The teacher models and records the mathematical representation on the board.

Phase 2 The teacher models again, eliciting responses from the students, and again records on the board.

Phase 3 Students work in pairs to do the mathematics and then the teacher, once again, records on the board.

Phase 4 Students work independently, monitored and supported by the teacher.

> 66 Interaction helps children clarify their ideas, get feedback on their thinking, and hear other points of view. Students can learn from one another as well as from their teachers. 99
>
> —**Marilyn Burns**

Student Interaction

Interactions allow students to make sense of what they are doing and help them to clarify, explain, and evaluate their thinking. Students take responsibility for their own learning as they attempt to understand a partner's reasoning. When students explain their reasoning to others, they learn to think metacognitively, organize their thoughts, and clearly communicate their ideas (Chapin et al., 2003).

In *Do The Math*, student interaction occurs in whole group, small group, and pairs as students work together to solve problems, play games, and explain their thinking.

- Think, Pair, Share provides a safe way for students to share ideas, clarify thinking, and prepare for class discussions.

- Lessons prompt teachers to partner students as they complete independent *WorkSpace* assignments.

- Partner games encourage active engagement and mathematical communication.

Meaningful Practice

Opportunities for repeated practice and application are essential to strengthen and reinforce students' learning (Gee, 2003; Marzano, 2002). Meaningful practice requires students to apply understandings rather than rely on rote procedures to solve problems. Essential concepts become meaningful when students connect new knowledge to existing knowledge, and solve problems with a thorough understanding of number and operations.

Practice is an essential part of every *Do The Math* lesson—in partner work, written practice in the *WorkSpace*, and games that reinforce math skills. The written practice in the *WorkSpace* always connects to the lesson and practice assignments never require new knowledge or skills for success.

Vocabulary and Language

Many words that describe mathematical ideas are familiar to students, but their common meanings are often very different from their mathematical meanings. Teaching the precise meanings of math vocabulary words supports the development of accurate conceptual knowledge and mathematical thinking (Raiker, 2002).

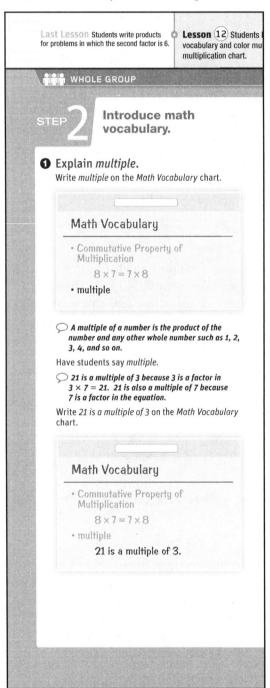

Teacher Guide, Multiplication B

The start of each *Do The Math* lesson highlights key vocabulary and provides Spanish translations. Lessons explicitly teach vocabulary using a step-by-step routine after students experience and develop a firm understanding of the concept. Vocabulary becomes meaningful as students connect new words to known math concepts.

Do The Math uses a three-step instructional process for teaching vocabulary:

❶ Students experience the math concept over the course of several lessons.

❷ The teacher explicitly teaches the vocabulary words using the *see it, hear it, say it, write it, read it* instructional routine.

❸ Students have many opportunities to use the vocabulary words during the lessons to ensure that they become part of their receptive and expressive vocabularies.

Assessment and Differentiation

Providing teachers with specific information on how each student is performing consistently enhances students' achievement in math (Baker et al., 2002). The goal of differentiated instruction is to meet the needs of all students. Formative assessment allows teachers to achieve this goal by identifying students who are struggling and students who need additional challenges.

Formative assessments are built into *Do The Math* to help teachers identify students' needs and differentiate instruction.

- The Beginning-of-Module Assessment places students in the correct module.

- Progress monitoring occurs after every fifth lesson to provide immediate support for students who need it.

- Suggestions for providing students additional support or added challenge are available at the end of every fifth lesson.

- Daily observations ensure that students receive the continuous guidance needed to successfully complete assignments.

- The End-of-Module Assessment is a summative assessment that measures student growth and determines readiness for the next module.

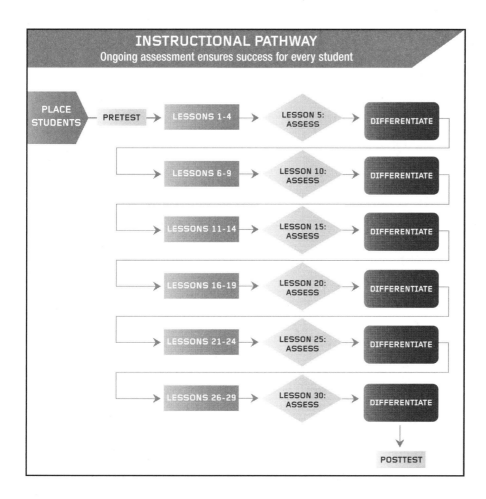

INSTRUCTIONAL PATHWAY
Ongoing assessment ensures success for every student

PLACE STUDENTS → PRETEST → LESSONS 1–4 → LESSON 5: ASSESS → DIFFERENTIATE

LESSONS 6–9 → LESSON 10: ASSESS → DIFFERENTIATE

LESSONS 11–14 → LESSON 15: ASSESS → DIFFERENTIATE

LESSONS 16–19 → LESSON 20: ASSESS → DIFFERENTIATE

LESSONS 21–24 → LESSON 25: ASSESS → DIFFERENTIATE

LESSONS 26–29 → LESSON 30: ASSESS → DIFFERENTIATE

POSTTEST

Reflecting on Instructional Strategies

Use the chart below to record questions and reflect on the *Do The Math* research-based strategies.

Instructional Strategy	Questions	Reflection
Scaffolded Content		
Explicit Instruction		
Multiple Strategies		
Gradual Release		
Student Interaction		
Meaningful Practice		
Vocabulary and Language		
Assessment and Differentiation		

Addition & Subtraction

In the previous two lessons, students practice solving comparing problems. During this lesson, students generate a list of comparing words, practice using the words to write questions for problems, and write and solve comparing word problems.

What's the Question? What's the Answer?

DIRECTIONS

➤ Write a question for each problem.
➤ Draw an open number line to solve the problem.
➤ Write the equation and difference.

(1) My dog weighs 44 pounds.
My cat weighs 12 pounds.

_____?

Open Number Line	Equation	Difference

(2) The high temperature today is 65 degrees.
The high temperature yesterday was 72 degrees.

_____?

Open Number Line	Equation	Difference

(3) Use the following numbers to complete the problem: 21, 36.

The home team's score was _____.

The visiting team's score was _____.

_____?

Open Number Line	Equation	Difference

Home Note: Your child solves comparing subtraction problems by drawing open number lines and writing equations.

Lesson 18 | 35

WorkSpace, **Addition & Subtraction B**

(4) Use the following numbers to complete the problem: 56, 72.

Perla is _____ inches tall.

Carla is _____ inches tall.

_____?

Open Number Line	Equation	Difference

(5) Write your own comparing problem about money.

My numbers are _____, _____.

_____

_____

_____

_____?

Open Number Line	Equation	Difference

36 | Lesson 18

Home Note: Your child writes comparing word problems and solves them.

WorkSpace, **Addition & Subtraction B**

Multiplication

This lesson begins with a review of how to draw rectangles to represent multiplication problems. Then students learn to find products greater than 36 by splitting rectangles.

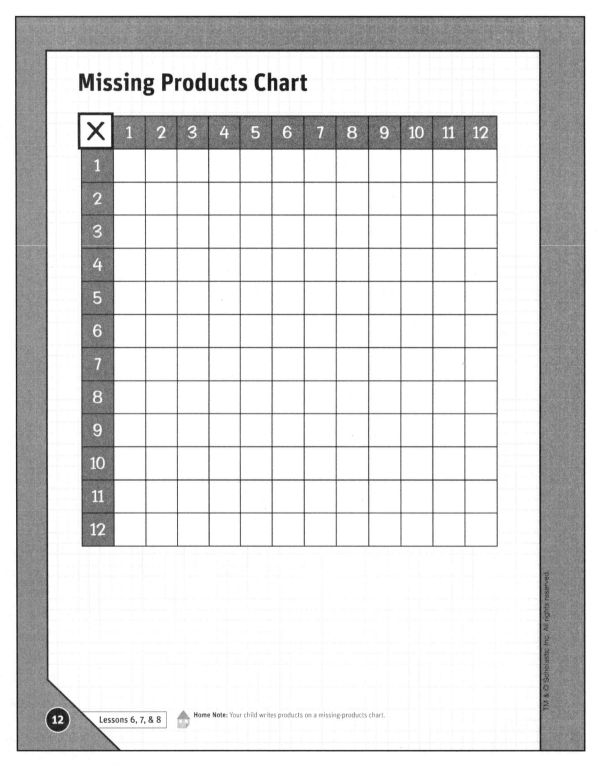

Missing Products Chart

X	1	2	3	4	5	6	7	8	9	10	11	12
1												
2												
3												
4												
5												
6												
7												
8												
9												
10												
11												
12												

(12)   Lessons 6, 7, & 8   **Home Note:** Your child writes products on a missing-products chart.

WorkSpace, **Multiplication B**

Draw Rectangles and Figure Out Products

DIRECTIONS

➤ Draw a rectangle for each multiplication problem below.
➤ Refer to the directions on page 16, if necessary.
➤ Write the product for each rectangle on your missing-products chart on page 12.

8×4　　　　　10×6　　　　　9×5

Home Note: Your child draws rectangles and writes equations for them.

Lesson 8　　**21**

WorkSpace, **Multiplication B**

Division

In the previous lessons, students learn to solve long division problems using related multiplication facts. During this lesson, students look for groups of 10 in the dividend to solve division problems that are not easily solved with a multiplication fact.

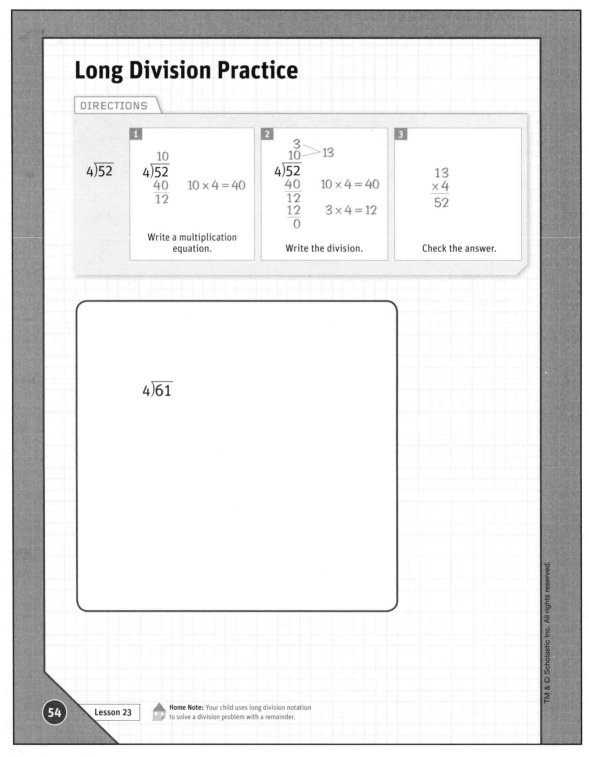

Long Division Practice

DIRECTIONS

1

$4\overline{)52}$

$\begin{array}{r} 10 \\ 4\overline{)52} \\ 40 \\ \hline 12 \end{array}$ $10 \times 4 = 40$

Write a multiplication equation.

2

$\begin{array}{r} 3 \\ 10 \end{array}\!\!\!> 13$

$\begin{array}{r} 4\overline{)52} \\ 40 \\ \hline 12 \\ 12 \\ \hline 0 \end{array}$ $10 \times 4 = 40$

$3 \times 4 = 12$

Write the division.

3

$\begin{array}{r} 13 \\ \times\ 4 \\ \hline 52 \end{array}$

Check the answer.

$4\overline{)61}$

🏠 **Home Note:** Your child uses long division notation to solve a division problem with a remainder.

WorkSpace, **Division B**

More Long Division Practice

DIRECTIONS

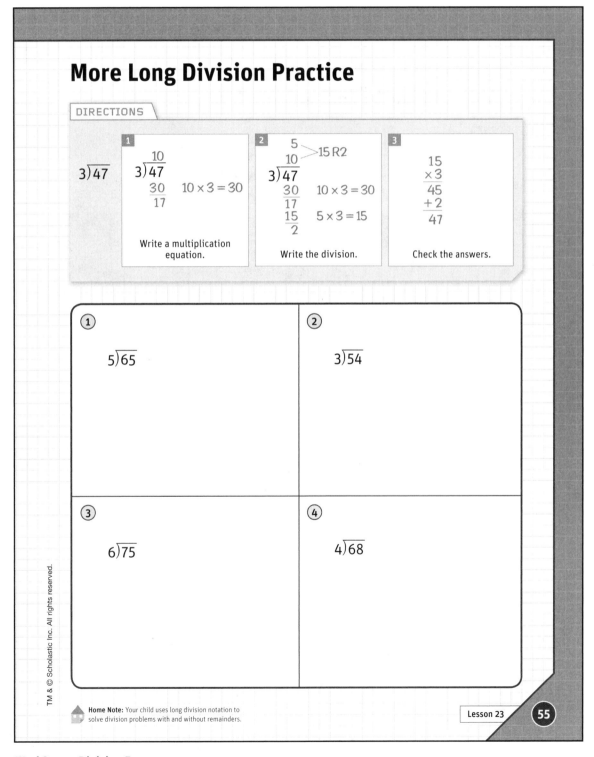

1

$3\overline{)47}$

$3\overline{)47}$
  $\underline{30}$ $10 \times 3 = 30$
  17

$\begin{array}{r} 10 \\ \end{array}$

Write a multiplication equation.

2

$3\overline{)47}$ $>15\,R2$
  $\underline{30}$ $10 \times 3 = 30$
  17
  $\underline{15}$ $5 \times 3 = 15$
  2

$\begin{array}{r} 5 \\ 10 \end{array}$

Write the division.

3

$\begin{array}{r} 15 \\ \times\,3 \\ \hline 45 \\ +\,2 \\ \hline 47 \end{array}$

Check the answers.

①

$5\overline{)65}$

②

$3\overline{)54}$

③

$6\overline{)75}$

④

$4\overline{)68}$

Home Note: Your child uses long division notation to solve division problems with and without remainders.

Lesson 23 · **55**

WorkSpace, **Division B**

Fractions

In previous lessons, students learn three different strategies to compare fractions. During this lesson, students learn a new strategy—comparing fractions that are one unit fraction from 1 whole.

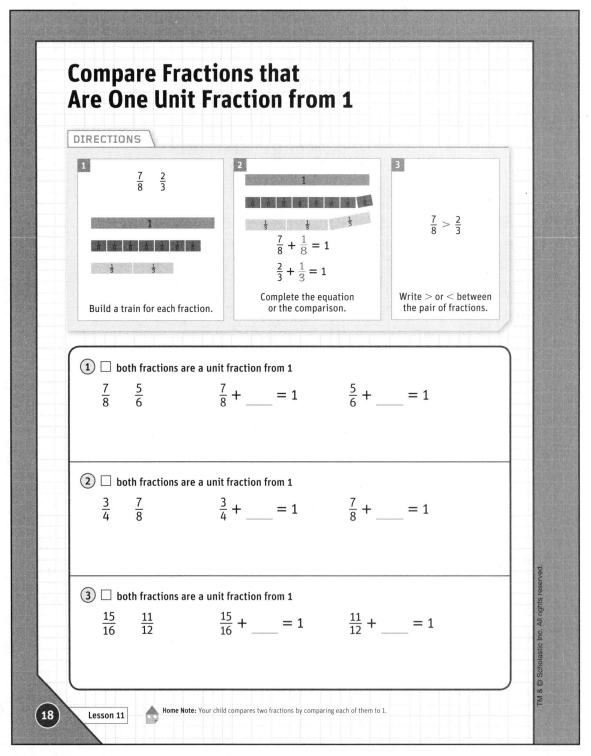

Compare Fractions that Are One Unit Fraction from 1

DIRECTIONS

1

$\frac{7}{8}$ $\frac{2}{3}$

1

$\frac{1}{3}$ $\frac{1}{3}$

Build a train for each fraction.

2

1

$\frac{7}{8} + \frac{1}{8} = 1$

$\frac{2}{3} + \frac{1}{3} = 1$

Complete the equation or the comparison.

3

$\frac{7}{8} > \frac{2}{3}$

Write > or < between the pair of fractions.

---

1 ☐ both fractions are a unit fraction from 1

$\frac{7}{8}$ $\frac{5}{6}$ $\frac{7}{8} + \underline{\quad} = 1$ $\frac{5}{6} + \underline{\quad} = 1$

---

2 ☐ both fractions are a unit fraction from 1

$\frac{3}{4}$ $\frac{7}{8}$ $\frac{3}{4} + \underline{\quad} = 1$ $\frac{7}{8} + \underline{\quad} = 1$

---

3 ☐ both fractions are a unit fraction from 1

$\frac{15}{16}$ $\frac{11}{12}$ $\frac{15}{16} + \underline{\quad} = 1$ $\frac{11}{12} + \underline{\quad} = 1$

---

(18)   Lesson 11   🏠 **Home Note:** Your child compares two fractions by comparing each of them to 1.

WorkSpace, **Fractions B**

Compare Fractions

DIRECTIONS

➤ Use these strategies to compare each pair of fractions.

Strategy 1: compare unit fractions $\frac{1}{6} > \frac{1}{8}$

Strategy 2: compare fractions with common numerators $\frac{3}{12} < \frac{3}{4}$

Strategy 3: compare fractions with common denominators $\frac{1}{4} < \frac{2}{4}$

Strategy 4: compare fractions one unit fraction from 1 whole $\frac{7}{8} < \frac{5}{6}$

➤ Write $<$ or $>$ between each pair.

① $\frac{1}{12}$ $\frac{1}{10}$

② $\frac{3}{4}$ $\frac{3}{6}$

③ $\frac{2}{5}$ $\frac{3}{5}$

④ $\frac{5}{8}$ $\frac{5}{6}$

⑤ $\frac{11}{12}$ $\frac{7}{8}$

⑥ $\frac{7}{12}$ $\frac{7}{16}$

⑦ $\frac{3}{4}$ $\frac{15}{16}$

⑧ $\frac{1}{16}$ $\frac{1}{15}$

 Home Note: Your child compares fractions using four strategies he or she has learned.

Lesson 11   **19**

WorkSpace, **Fractions B**

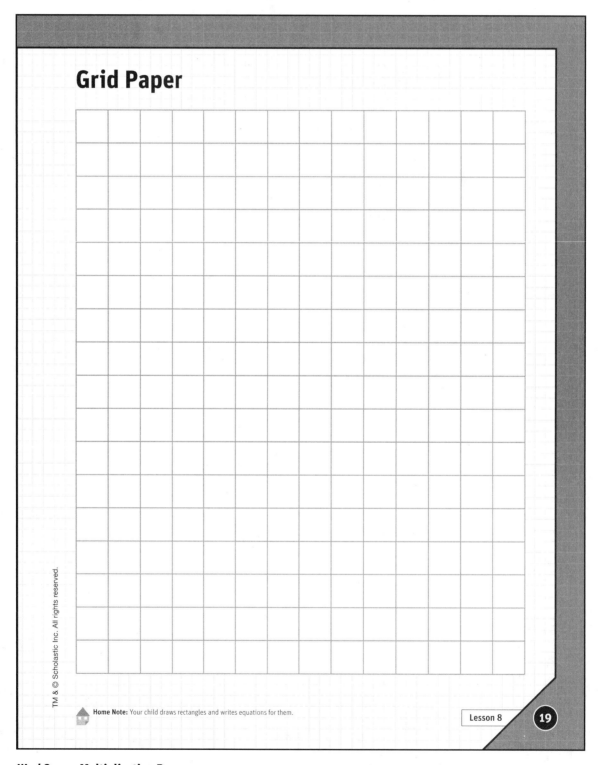

Grid Paper

Home Note: Your child draws rectangles and writes equations for them.

Lesson 8   19

WorkSpace, **Multiplication B**

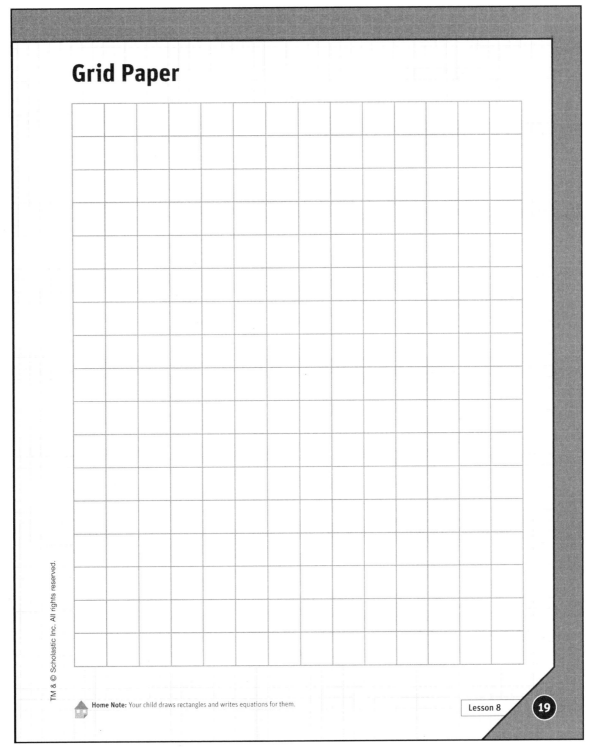

Grid Paper

Home Note: Your child draws rectangles and writes equations for them.

Lesson 8 **19**

WorkSpace, **Multiplication B**

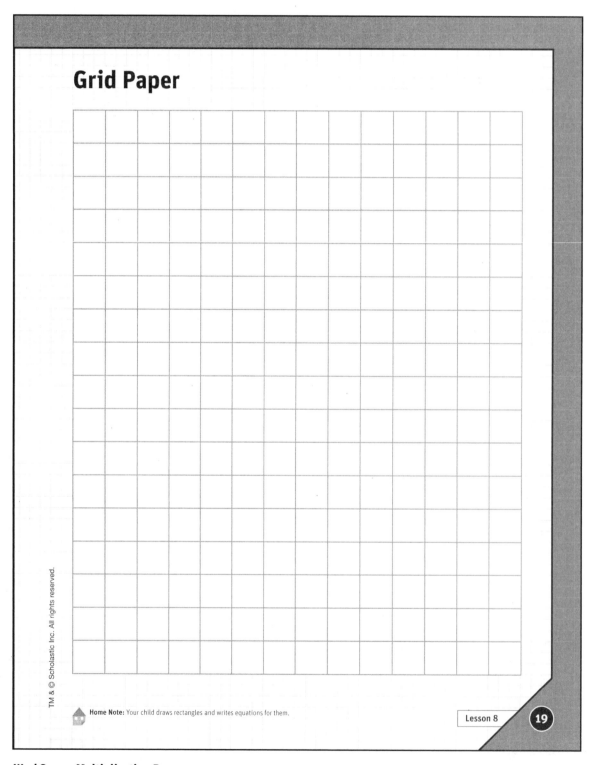

Grid Paper

Home Note: Your child draws rectangles and writes equations for them.

Lesson 8   **19**

WorkSpace, **Multiplication B**

Module at a Glance

Each of the 12 modules in *Do The Math* begins with a preliminary assessment of student knowledge of the topic, followed by 30 step-by-step lessons on that topic, and concludes with a summative assessment to measure student growth.

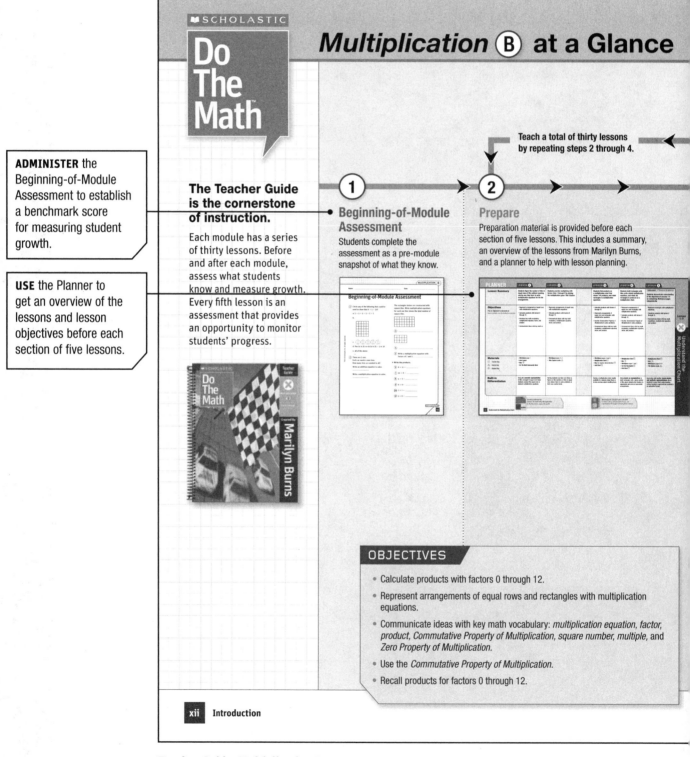

ADMINISTER the Beginning-of-Module Assessment to establish a benchmark score for measuring student growth.

USE the Planner to get an overview of the lessons and lesson objectives before each section of five lessons.

SCHOLASTIC

Do The Math™

Multiplication Ⓑ at a Glance

The Teacher Guide is the cornerstone of instruction.

Each module has a series of thirty lessons. Before and after each module, assess what students know and measure growth. Every fifth lesson is an assessment that provides an opportunity to monitor students' progress.

Teach a total of thirty lessons by repeating steps 2 through 4.

①

Beginning-of-Module Assessment

Students complete the assessment as a pre-module snapshot of what they know.

②

Prepare

Preparation material is provided before each section of five lessons. This includes a summary, an overview of the lessons from Marilyn Burns, and a planner to help with lesson planning.

OBJECTIVES

- Calculate products with factors 0 through 12.
- Represent arrangements of equal rows and rectangles with multiplication equations.
- Communicate ideas with key math vocabulary: *multiplication equation, factor, product, Commutative Property of Multiplication, square number, multiple,* and *Zero Property of Multiplication.*
- Use the *Commutative Property of Multiplication.*
- Recall products for factors 0 through 12.

xii Introduction

Teacher Guide, Multiplication B

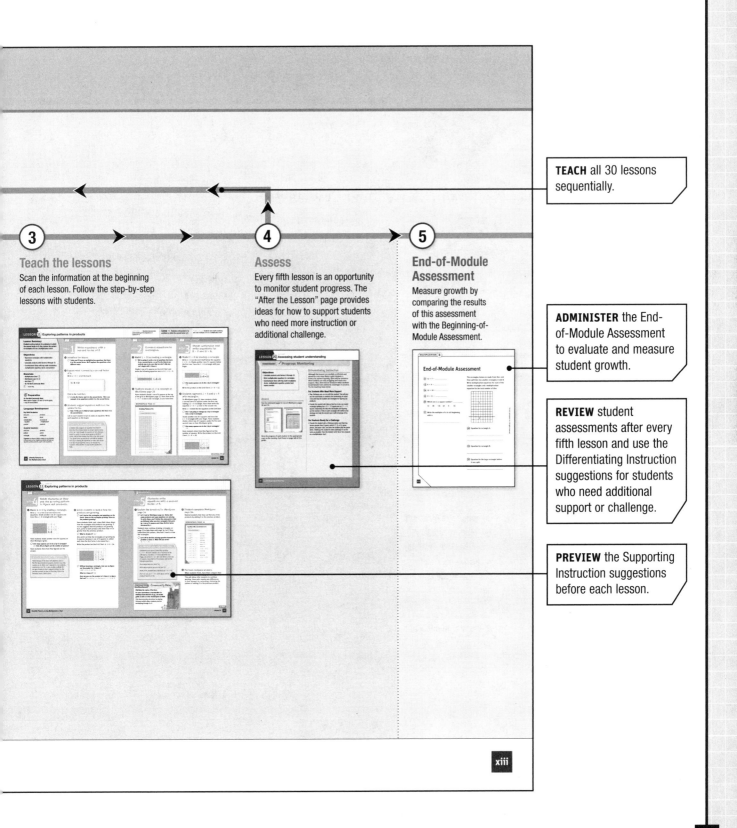

TEACH all 30 lessons sequentially.

3
Teach the lessons
Scan the information at the beginning of each lesson. Follow the step-by-step lessons with students.

4
Assess
Every fifth lesson is an opportunity to monitor student progress. The "After the Lesson" page provides ideas for how to support students who need more instruction or additional challenge.

5
End-of-Module Assessment
Measure growth by comparing the results of this assessment with the Beginning-of-Module Assessment.

ADMINISTER the End-of-Module Assessment to evaluate and measure student growth.

REVIEW student assessments after every fifth lesson and use the Differentiating Instruction suggestions for students who need additional support or challenge.

PREVIEW the Supporting Instruction suggestions before each lesson.

xiii

Professional Support From Marilyn Burns

A letter from Marilyn Burns before each group of five lessons introduces key concepts and clarifies objectives for the upcoming lessons.

FROM MARILYN BURNS

READ the letter to understand the sequence and rationale for the group of lessons.

Dear Colleague,

In these lessons, students focus on the multiplication chart and the connections between multiplication equations and rectangles.

The first lesson raises a question for students: *Suppose all of the numbers on the multiplication chart suddenly disappeared?* A second question focuses students on the intent of the lessons in this section: *How can we use the rectangles we've been exploring to help us enter the products correctly on the chart?*

Each student has a blank 12-by-12 grid titled *Missing Products*. Throughout the lessons, through hands-on experiences with rectangles, students write products on their grids to recreate the multiplication chart.

REVIEW the main objectives for the next five lessons.

In Lessons 6–10, students...

• Calculate products with factors 0 through 12.

• Represent arrangements of equal rows and rectangles with multiplication equations.

• Communicate ideas with key math vocabulary: *multiplication equation*, *factor*, *product*, and *Commutative Property of Multiplication*.

• Use the *Commutative Property of Multiplication* to solve problems.

X	1	2	3	4	5	6	7	8	9	10	11	12
1									9			12
2					12							
3				12								
4			12									
5												
6		12										
7												
8												
9	9											
10												
11												
12	12											

26 Understand the Multiplication Chart

Teacher Guide, Multiplication B

Students learn the strategy of "rectangle splitting" to figure out products, which informally introduces them to the Distributive Property of Multiplication over Addition.

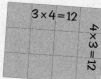

35

14

14

35 + 14 + 14 = 63

These lessons help deepen students' understanding of multiplication while helping build their number sense and familiarity with products up to 12 × 12. Also, while students already know that the order of factors does not affect the products; that is, that 4 × 3 and 3 × 4 both have the same product, ere they are formally introduced to naming it as the Commutative Property f Multiplication.

3 × 4 = 12

4 × 3 = 12

66 These lessons help deepen students' understanding of multiplication while helping build their number sense and familiarity with products up to 12 × 12. 99

Lessons
6–10

❌

Understand the Multiplication Chart

PINPOINT which five lessons are taught in this section.

Using the Planner

Refer to the planner before each group of five lessons for an overall picture of how the lessons progress and build upon each other.

PREVIEW the Lesson Summary for a brief overview of each lesson.

REVIEW the Objectives listed for each lesson.

GATHER *Do The Math* materials and any additional classroom supplies needed for the lesson.

BROADEN your understanding of the topic by reading suggested pages in *Teaching Arithmetic*.

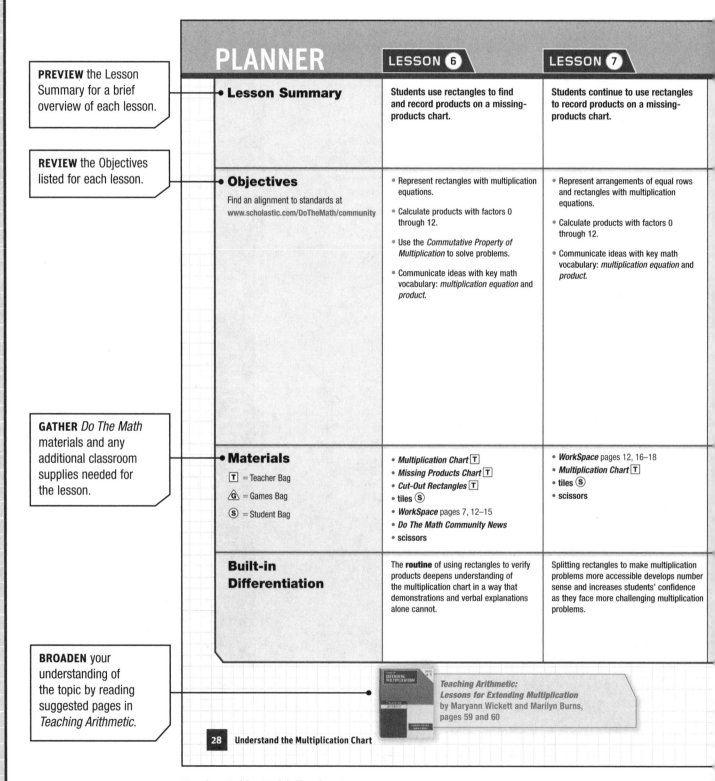

PLANNER	LESSON **6**	LESSON **7**
Lesson Summary	Students use rectangles to find and record products on a missing-products chart.	Students continue to use rectangles to record products on a missing-products chart.
Objectives Find an alignment to standards at www.scholastic.com/DoTheMath/community	• Represent rectangles with multiplication equations. • Calculate products with factors 0 through 12. • Use the *Commutative Property of Multiplication* to solve problems. • Communicate ideas with key math vocabulary: *multiplication equation* and *product*.	• Represent arrangements of equal rows and rectangles with multiplication equations. • Calculate products with factors 0 through 12. • Communicate ideas with key math vocabulary: *multiplication equation* and *product*.
Materials T = Teacher Bag G = Games Bag S = Student Bag	• *Multiplication Chart* T • *Missing Products Chart* T • *Cut-Out Rectangles* T • tiles S • *WorkSpace* pages 7, 12–15 • *Do The Math Community News* • scissors	• *WorkSpace* pages 12, 16–18 • *Multiplication Chart* T • tiles S • scissors
Built-in Differentiation	The **routine** of using rectangles to verify products deepens understanding of the multiplication chart in a way that demonstrations and verbal explanations alone cannot.	Splitting rectangles to make multiplication problems more accessible develops number sense and increases students' confidence as they face more challenging multiplication problems.

Teaching Arithmetic: Lessons for Extending Multiplication by Maryann Wickett and Marilyn Burns, pages 59 and 60

28 **Understand the Multiplication Chart**

Teacher Guide, Multiplication B

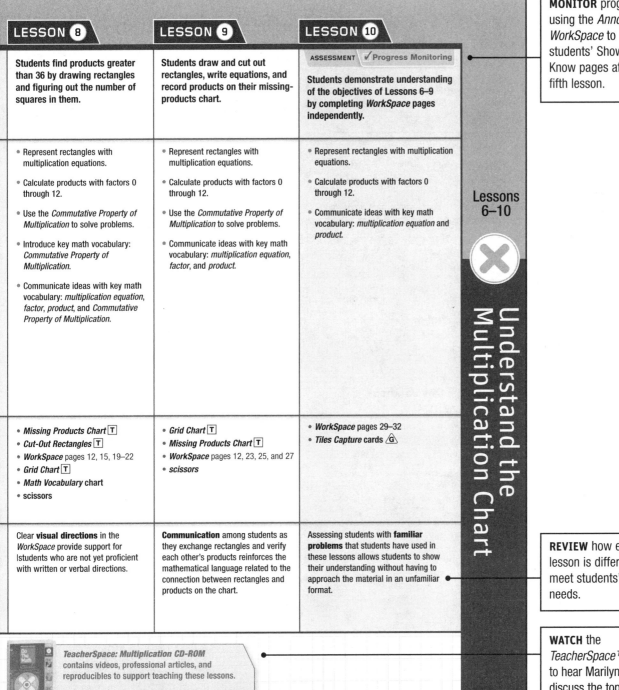

LESSON 8	LESSON 9	LESSON 10
		ASSESSMENT ✓ Progress Monitoring
Students find products greater than 36 by drawing rectangles and figuring out the number of squares in them.	Students draw and cut out rectangles, write equations, and record products on their missing-products chart.	Students demonstrate understanding of the objectives of Lessons 6–9 by completing *WorkSpace* pages independently.
• Represent rectangles with multiplication equations. • Calculate products with factors 0 through 12. • Use the *Commutative Property of Multiplication* to solve problems. • Introduce key math vocabulary: *Commutative Property of Multiplication*. • Communicate ideas with key math vocabulary: *multiplication equation, factor, product,* and *Commutative Property of Multiplication*.	• Represent rectangles with multiplication equations. • Calculate products with factors 0 through 12. • Use the *Commutative Property of Multiplication* to solve problems. • Communicate ideas with key math vocabulary: *multiplication equation, factor,* and *product*.	• Represent rectangles with multiplication equations. • Calculate products with factors 0 through 12. • Communicate ideas with key math vocabulary: *multiplication equation* and *product*.
• *Missing Products Chart* T • *Cut-Out Rectangles* T • *WorkSpace* pages 12, 15, 19–22 • *Grid Chart* T • *Math Vocabulary* chart • scissors	• *Grid Chart* T • *Missing Products Chart* T • *WorkSpace* pages 12, 23, 25, and 27 • scissors	• *WorkSpace* pages 29–32 • *Tiles Capture* cards G
Clear **visual directions** in the *WorkSpace* provide support for lstudents who are not yet proficient with written or verbal directions.	**Communication** among students as they exchange rectangles and verify each other's products reinforces the mathematical language related to the connection between rectangles and products on the chart.	Assessing students with **familiar problems** that students have used in these lessons allows students to show their understanding without having to approach the material in an unfamiliar format.

TeacherSpace: Multiplication CD-ROM contains videos, professional articles, and reproducibles to support teaching these lessons.

Lessons 6–10

Understand the Multiplication Chart

MONITOR progress by using the *Annotated WorkSpace* to check students' Show What You Know pages after every fifth lesson.

REVIEW how each lesson is differentiated to meet students' various needs.

WATCH the *TeacherSpace™* videos to hear Marilyn Burns discuss the topic and see teachers demonstrate instructional strategies.

Teaching Addition & Subtraction

Every lesson in the Teacher Guide includes preparation suggestions, step-by-step instructions, careful scaffolding, and differentiation.

PREVIEW the mathematical objectives that are the focus of the lesson.

PREPARE charts before the lesson and keep them posted to record information during subsequent lessons.

USE translations of key words as needed to help Spanish-speaking students understand the lesson content.

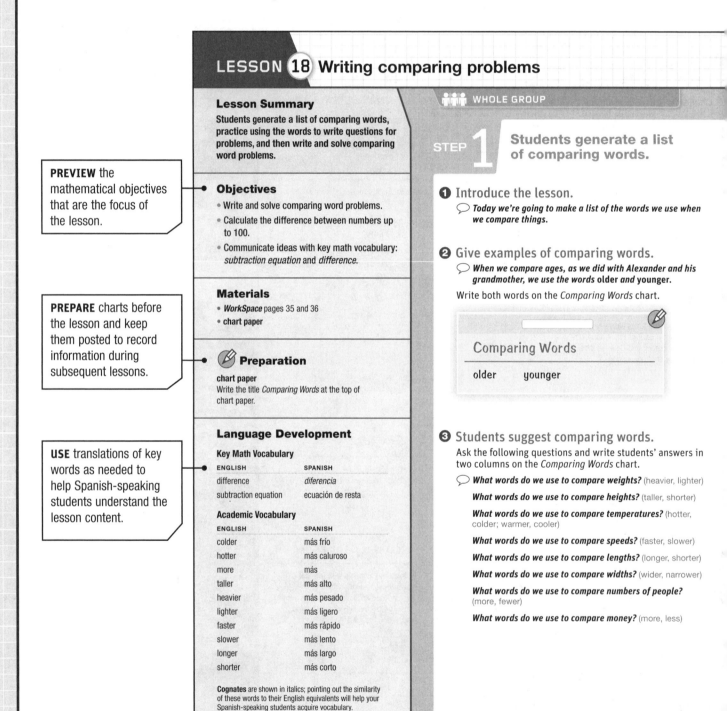

LESSON 18 Writing comparing problems

Lesson Summary

Students generate a list of comparing words, practice using the words to write questions for problems, and then write and solve comparing word problems.

Objectives

- Write and solve comparing word problems.
- Calculate the difference between numbers up to 100.
- Communicate ideas with key math vocabulary: *subtraction equation* and *difference*.

Materials

- *WorkSpace* pages 35 and 36
- chart paper

✏ Preparation

chart paper
Write the title *Comparing Words* at the top of chart paper.

Language Development

Key Math Vocabulary

ENGLISH	SPANISH
difference	*diferencia*
subtraction equation	ecuación de resta

Academic Vocabulary

ENGLISH	SPANISH
colder	más frío
hotter	más caluroso
more	más
taller	más alto
heavier	más pesado
lighter	más ligero
faster	más rápido
slower	más lento
longer	más largo
shorter	más corto

Cognates are shown in italics; pointing out the similarity of these words to their English equivalents will help your Spanish-speaking students acquire vocabulary.

82 Solve Take-Away and Comparing Problems

👤👤👤 WHOLE GROUP

STEP 1 Students generate a list of comparing words.

❶ **Introduce the lesson.**
💬 *Today we're going to make a list of the words we use when we compare things.*

❷ **Give examples of comparing words.**
💬 *When we compare ages, as we did with Alexander and his grandmother, we use the words older and younger.*
Write both words on the *Comparing Words* chart.

Comparing Words

older   younger

❸ **Students suggest comparing words.**
Ask the following questions and write students' answers in two columns on the *Comparing Words* chart.
💬 *What words do we use to compare weights?* (heavier, lighter)

What words do we use to compare heights? (taller, shorter)

What words do we use to compare temperatures? (hotter, colder; warmer, cooler)

What words do we use to compare speeds? (faster, slower)

What words do we use to compare lengths? (longer, shorter)

What words do we use to compare widths? (wider, narrower)

What words do we use to compare numbers of people? (more, fewer)

What words do we use to compare money? (more, less)

Teacher Guide, Addition & Subtraction B

Last Lesson Students continue to solve comparing problems.

Lesson (18) Students generate a list of comparing words and then write and solve comparing word problems.

Next Lesson Students review take-away and comparing problems, identify problems as one type or the other, and solve both types.

SITUATE the current lesson within the context of the last and next lessons.

NOTE the student grouping for each step of the lesson.

PARTNERS

👥 WHOLE GROUP

STEP **2** Guide students to write a question for a comparing problem.

Comparing Words

older	younger
heavier	lighter
taller	shorter
hotter	colder
warmer	cooler
faster	slower
longer	shorter
wider	narrower
more	fewer, less

❶ Read a problem situation.

Have students turn to *WorkSpace* page 35.

💬 *Now you'll write questions for some comparing problems.*

Read the first problem situation aloud.

What's the Question? What's the Answer?

> Write a question for each problem.
> Draw an open number line to solve the problem.
> Write the equation and difference.

① My dog weighs 66 pounds.
My cat weighs 12 pounds.

② The high temperature today is 93 degrees.
The high temperature yesterday was 72 degrees.

③ Use the following numbers to complete the problem: 21, 36.
The home team's score was ___.
The visiting team's score was ___.

💬 *Think about a comparing question we could ask for this situation.*

Have students think, pair, share. Write students' suggested questions on the board.

How much less does my cat weigh?

How much more does my dog weigh?

What is the difference between their weights?

Students' questions will vary but should be similar to the questions shown.

💬 *Choose one of the questions and write it on WorkSpace page 35.*

SUPPORTING INSTRUCTION

If students have difficulty coming up with comparing words for a particular category, prompt them with a specific example. For temperature, you could say, "On Saturday the high temperature was 75 degrees. On Sunday the high temperature was 68 degrees. Saturday was *blank* than Sunday. Sunday was *blank* than Saturday."

PREVIEW the Supporting Instruction boxes for alerts of potential stumbling blocks and helpful suggestions.

PROMPT students to think and share with a partner before reporting to the class.

CONTINUE

Teaching Addition & Subtraction

Each lesson follows the gradual-release model of instruction, providing the practice and support students need before working with the math concepts independently.

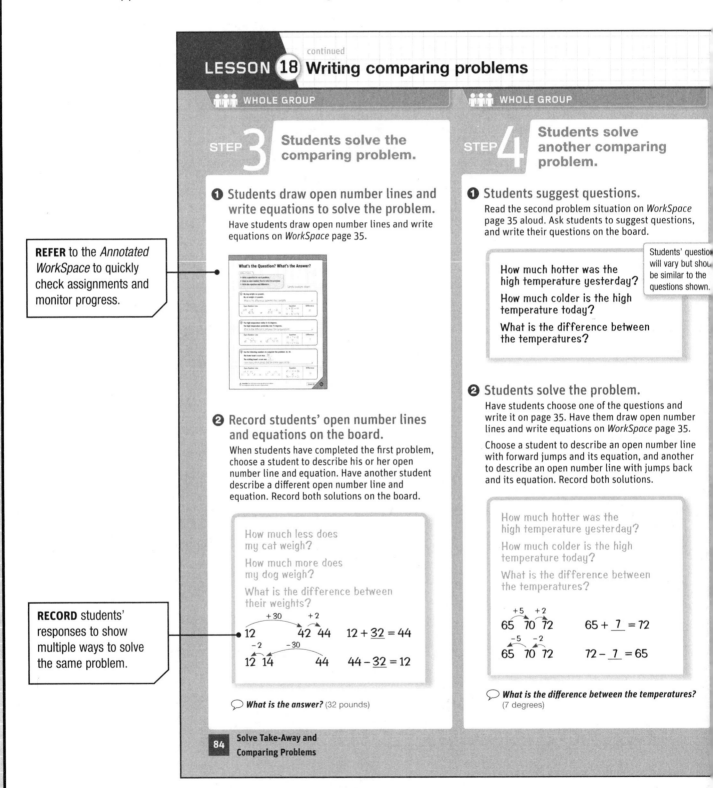

LESSON 18 continued **Writing comparing problems**

WHOLE GROUP

STEP 3 Students solve the comparing problem.

1 Students draw open number lines and write equations to solve the problem.

Have students draw open number lines and write equations on *WorkSpace* page 35.

REFER to the *Annotated WorkSpace* to quickly check assignments and monitor progress.

2 Record students' open number lines and equations on the board.

When students have completed the first problem, choose a student to describe his or her open number line and equation. Have another student describe a different open number line and equation. Record both solutions on the board.

RECORD students' responses to show multiple ways to solve the same problem.

How much less does my cat weigh?

How much more does my dog weigh?

What is the difference between their weights?

$$12 + \underline{32} = 44$$
$$44 - \underline{32} = 12$$

💬 *What is the answer?* (32 pounds)

84 Solve Take-Away and Comparing Problems

WHOLE GROUP

STEP 4 Students solve another comparing problem.

1 Students suggest questions.

Read the second problem situation on *WorkSpace* page 35 aloud. Ask students to suggest questions, and write their questions on the board.

How much hotter was the high temperature yesterday?

How much colder is the high temperature today?

What is the difference between the temperatures?

Students' questions will vary but should be similar to the questions shown.

2 Students solve the problem.

Have students choose one of the questions and write it on page 35. Have them draw open number lines and write equations on *WorkSpace* page 35.

Choose a student to describe an open number line with forward jumps and its equation, and another to describe an open number line with jumps back and its equation. Record both solutions.

How much hotter was the high temperature yesterday?

How much colder is the high temperature today?

What is the difference between the temperatures?

$$65 + \underline{7} = 72$$
$$72 - \underline{7} = 65$$

💬 *What is the difference between the temperatures?* (7 degrees)

Teacher Guide, Addition & Subtraction B

STEP 5 Guide students to complete comparing problem situations.

❶ **Partners complete a problem situation and write a question.**

💬 *For the third problem on page 35, you need to decide which number to put in which blank.*

Have partners work together to decide where to put each number and what question to write. (Students will solve the problem later.)

Choose a student to read his or her problem and question. Write the problem and question on the board.

Ask whether anyone put the numbers in different blanks or wrote a different question. Choose such a student to read his or her problem and question. Write them on the board.

> This is one example of a possible way to write the problem and question.

The home team's score was 36.

The visiting team's score was 21.

How many more points did the home team score?

❷ **Students complete another problem situation and write another question.**

Repeat the process, filling in the numbers and writing the question for problem 4 on *WorkSpace* page 36.

STEP 6 Students solve comparing problems.

❶ **Students complete *WorkSpace* pages 35 and 36.**

💬 *You've written the problems and questions for problems 3 and 4. Solve them using open number lines. For problem 5, choose your own numbers, write your own problem, and solve it with an open number line.*

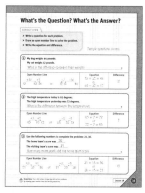

When students have completed the page, have them compare their open number lines, equations, and answers. Have students read the problem they wrote for item 5 to their partners, who should then solve the problem.

STOP

> **ENCOURAGE** students to check with each other as they complete *WorkSpace* assignments.

Teaching Multiplication

Well-planned lessons and scaffolded content ensure that all students develop a foundational understanding of multiplication.

LESSON 8 Using rectangles to figure products

REFER to the bar on the top of each step in the lesson to plan student groupings.

Lesson Summary

Students find products greater than 36 by drawing rectangles and figuring out the number of squares in them.

REVIEW the lesson objectives before teaching.

Objectives

* Represent rectangles with multiplication equations.
* Calculate products with factors 0 through 12.
* Use the *Commutative Property of Multiplication* to solve problems.
* Introduce key math vocabulary: *Commutative Property of Multiplication*
* Communicate ideas with key math vocabulary: *multiplication equation, factor, product*, and *Commutative Property of Multiplication*.

Materials

* *Missing Products Chart* T
* *Cut-Out Rectangles* T
* *WorkSpace* pages 12, 15, 19–22
* *Grid Chart* T
* *Math Vocabulary* chart
* scissors

T = Teacher Bag

Language Development

POINT OUT cognates to help Spanish-speaking students acquire math vocabulary in English.

Key Math Vocabulary

ENGLISH	SPANISH
factor	*factor*
Commutative Property of Multiplication	*propiedad conmutativa de la multiplicación*
multiplication equation	*ecuación de multiplicación*
product	*producto*

Academic Vocabulary

ENGLISH	SPANISH
row	*fila*
times	*por*

Cognates are shown in italics; pointing out the similarity of these words to their English equivalents will help your Spanish-speaking students acquire math vocabulary.

INTRODUCE Academic Vocabulary terms when needed to clarify the mathematical meaning of familiar words.

36 Understand the Multiplication Chart

👥 WHOLE GROUP

STEP 1 Model how to find the product of 8 × 7 by splitting the related rectangle.

❶ **Introduce the lesson.**

💬 *Today you'll continue making rectangles and writing their products on your missing-products charts.*

❷ **Demonstrate how to split a rectangle.**

💬 *I can use a rectangle to find a product. Watch as I draw a rectangle to match 8 times 7.*

Draw an 8-by-7 rectangle on the *Grid Chart*.

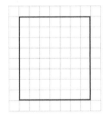

💬 *One way to figure out the product of 8 times 7 is to count all the squares. Another way that I'd like you to learn is called rectangle splitting. Watch as I split the rectangle I drew to make it easier to figure out how many squares there are.*

Draw a line to split the rectangle into an 8 × 5 rectangle and an 8 × 2 rectangle.

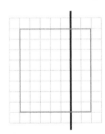

💬 *I split the rectangle so that I can count by 5s and by 2s to figure out how many squares there are.*

Teacher Guide, Multiplication B

Last Lesson Students continue to use rectangles to record products on a missing-products chart.

Lesson (8) Students find products greater than 36 by drawing rectangles and figuring out the number of squares in them.

Next Lesson Students make rectangles with dimensions up to 12 × 12 and continue to write products on their missing-products chart.

REVIEW how the current lesson relates to the last and next lessons.

❸ **Use rectangle splitting to figure out the product.**

Have students count with you by 5s, and write *40* below the left rectangle. Then have them count with you by 2s, and write *16* below the right rectangle. Have students add 40 and 16 and say the answer together. (56) Write *8 × 7 = 56* below the rectangle.

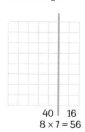

40 | 16
8 × 7 = 56

❹ **Demonstrate another way to split the rectangle.**

💬 *Now I'll split the rectangle another way so that I can still count by 5s and 2s.*

Erase the line on the rectangle, and draw two new lines, as shown.

Have students count by 5s, 2s, and 1s to find the number of squares in each rectangle, and write the number. Then have students add the numbers to verify the product 56.

35

14

7

❺ **Check and write the product.**

Check the product by placing the 8 × 7 cut-out rectangle on the *Multiplication Chart*. Write the equation 8 × 7 = 56 on the rectangle.

Place the rectangle on the *Missing Products Chart*. Lift the lower-right corner and write 56.

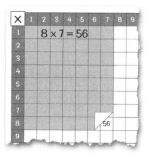

❻ **Students draw an 8-by-7 rectangle.**

💬 *Draw an 8-by-7 rectangle on WorkSpace page 19. Start at the top left square, because you'll need the rest of the room on the grid later. Write the equation inside the rectangle, and cut it out. Use the rectangle to check the product on your multiplication chart on page 15. Then write the product on your missing-products chart on page 12.*

CONTINUE ▷

Lesson 8   37

DEMONSTRATE the strategy multiple ways before asking students to try it independently.

Teaching Multiplication

Students achieve deeper understanding of concepts as they learn different strategies and develop multiple approaches to solving math problems.

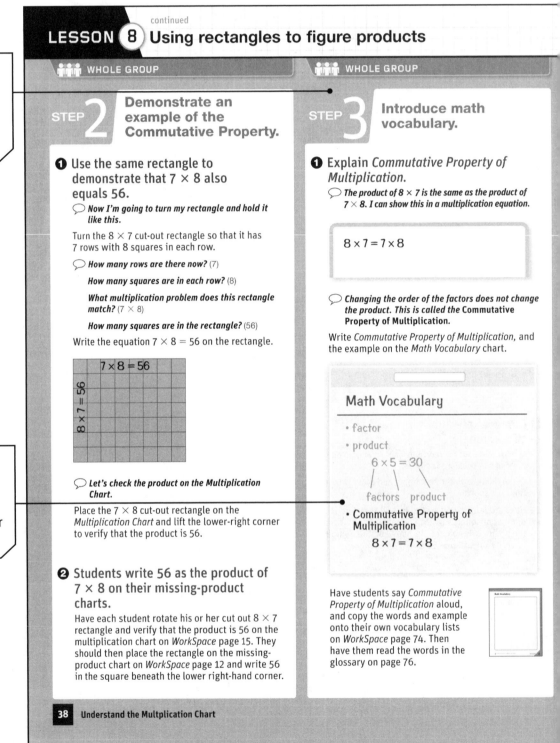

LESSON 8 continued **Using rectangles to figure products**

TEACH math vocabulary using the *see it, hear it, say it, write it, read it* routine after students have experienced the concept.

RECORD words on the class *Math Vocabulary* chart and prompt students to write each word in the back of their *WorkSpace* books.

👥 WHOLE GROUP

STEP 2 Demonstrate an example of the Commutative Property.

❶ Use the same rectangle to demonstrate that 7 × 8 also equals 56.

💬 *Now I'm going to turn my rectangle and hold it like this.*

Turn the 8 × 7 cut-out rectangle so that it has 7 rows with 8 squares in each row.

💬 *How many rows are there now?* (7)

How many squares are in each row? (8)

What multiplication problem does this rectangle match? (7 × 8)

How many squares are in the rectangle? (56)

Write the equation 7 × 8 = 56 on the rectangle.

💬 *Let's check the product on the Multiplication Chart.*

Place the 7 × 8 cut-out rectangle on the *Multiplication Chart* and lift the lower-right corner to verify that the product is 56.

❷ Students write 56 as the product of 7 × 8 on their missing-product charts.

Have each student rotate his or her cut out 8 × 7 rectangle and verify that the product is 56 on the multiplication chart on *WorkSpace* page 15. They should then place the rectangle on the missing-product chart on *WorkSpace* page 12 and write 56 in the square beneath the lower right-hand corner.

38 Understand the Multplication Chart

👥 WHOLE GROUP

STEP 3 Introduce math vocabulary.

❶ Explain *Commutative Property of Multiplication*.

💬 *The product of 8 × 7 is the same as the product of 7 × 8. I can show this in a multiplication equation.*

8 × 7 = 7 × 8

💬 *Changing the order of the factors does not change the product. This is called the* **Commutative Property of Multiplication.**

Write *Commutative Property of Multiplication*, and the example on the *Math Vocabulary* chart.

Math Vocabulary

• factor
• product

6 × 5 = 30

factors   product

• **Commutative Property of Multiplication**

8 × 7 = 7 × 8

Have students say *Commutative Property of Multiplication* aloud, and copy the words and example onto their own vocabulary lists on *WorkSpace* page 74. Then have them read the words in the glossary on page 76.

Teacher Guide, Multiplication B

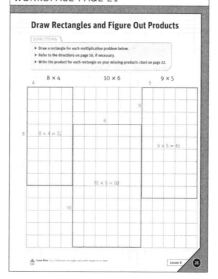

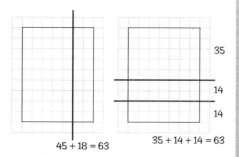

WHOLE GROUP

STEP 4 — Demonstrate finding a product by rectangle splitting.

❶ Show two ways to figure 9 × 7.

💬 *Draw a 9-by-7 rectangle on WorkSpace page 19. It should have 9 rows with 7 squares in each row.*

Demonstrate one way to split the 9-by-7 rectangle as shown on the left below. Count by 5s and then by 2s. Write each total and then add.

Next, redraw the rectangle and split it as shown on the right below. Again, count by 5s and then by 2s. Write each total and then add. Then have students write 9 × 7 = 63 in the rectangles they have drawn.

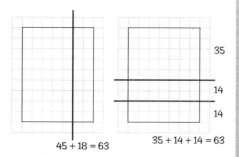

45 + 18 = 63

35
14
14

35 + 14 + 14 = 63

❷ Students verify that 9 × 7 = 63 and 7 × 9 = 63.

Have students cut out and place their 9 × 7 rectangles on their multiplication charts. Then have them place the rectangles on their missing-products charts and write the product.

💬 *Now turn your 9-by-7 rectangle so that it has 7 rows with 9 squares in each row. Do the same as you did for the 9-by-7 rectangle.*

INDIVIDUALS

STEP 5 — Students make more rectangles and figure out their products.

❶ Students work independently on *WorkSpace* page 21.

Have students turn to *WorkSpace* page 21 and explain the directions. (It's fine if there isn't enough time for this, as students will do similar exercises in subsequent lessons.)

WORKSPACE PAGE 21

Draw Rectangles and Figure Out Products

DIRECTIONS
▸ Draw a rectangle for each multiplication problem below.
▸ Refer to the directions on page 16, if necessary.
▸ Write the product for each rectangle on your missing-products chart on page 12.

8 × 4   10 × 6   9 × 5

8 × 4 = 32

9 × 5 = 45

10 × 6 = 60

Lesson 8 21

❷ Students check their equations and charts with a partner.

Have partners check the work of their partners, seeing whether they wrote the same equations and placed the products in the same squares of their charts.

> **MODEL** multiple ways for students to arrive at the same answer.

> **PAIR** students to compare their equations and products.

STOP

Lesson 8 **39**

Teaching Division

Carefully scaffolded lessons help students understand the concept of division and how it relates to multiplication.

LESSON 23 Solving division problems with partial quotients

REVIEW the Lesson Summary and Objectives for a quick overview.

Lesson Summary
Students solve problems using long division for two-digit dividends and one-digit divisors.

Objectives
- Use the inverse relationship between division and multiplication to solve problems.
- Calculate the quotients and remainders for two-digit dividends and one-digit divisors.
- Communicate ideas with key math vocabulary: *dividend, divisor, quotient,* and *remainder.*

Materials
- *WorkSpace* pages 54 and 55

TEACH key words using the *see it, hear it, say it, write it, read it* routine.

Language Development

Key Math Vocabulary

ENGLISH	SPANISH
dividend	*dividendo*
divisor	*divisor*
quotient	*cociente*
remainder	residuo

Academic Vocabulary

ENGLISH	SPANISH
multiplication equation	*ecuación de multiplicación*

Cognates are shown in italics; pointing out the similarity of these words to their English equivalents will help your Spanish-speaking students acquire vocabulary.

USE the scripted dialogue to ensure precise and consistent use of math language.

WHOLE GROUP

STEP 1 Demonstrate solving a division problem by taking out 10s.

❶ **Introduce the lesson.**

💬 *Today we will continue to solve division problems using long division.*

❷ **Present a problem.**

Write the long division for $42 \div 3$ on the board.

$$3\overline{)42}$$

💬 *To solve the problem, I can write the related multiplication, but it doesn't help me because I don't know what number times 3 is 42.*

I do know that there are at least 10 groups of 3 in 42. I know that because $10 \times 3 = 30$ and 30 is less than 42.

Record the multiplication equation, 10 in the quotient and 30 under 42.

$$\begin{array}{r} 10 \\ 3\overline{)42} \\ \underline{30} \end{array} \qquad 10 \times 3 = 30$$

💬 *When I subtract I get 12. Then I think: What number times 3 is 12? I know that 4 times 3 equals 12, so I can write 4 above the 10.*

$$\begin{array}{r} 4 \\ 10 \\ 3\overline{)42} \\ \underline{30} \qquad 10 \times 3 = 30 \\ 12 \\ \underline{12} \qquad 4 \times 3 = 12 \\ 0 \end{array}$$

106 Calculate Quotients and Remainders

Teacher Guide, Division B

Last lesson Students continue to use long division to solve division problems, now with remainders.

Lesson (23) Students solve problems using long division for two-digit dividends and one-digit divisors.

Next Lesson Students play a division game that gives them practice dividing two-digit dividends by one-digit divisors.

REVIEW snapshots of the previous lesson, current lesson, and next lesson.

👤👤👤 WHOLE GROUP

STEP **2** **Demonstrate a second example.**

RECORD the steps for solving a problem for students to refer to as they work independently on similar problems.

❸ **Demonstrate how to figure the answer.**

💬 *We have 10 groups of 3 in 42 and another 4 groups of 3 in 42. In all, that is 14 groups of 3 in 42.*

Draw lines from 4 and 10 and write 14.

```
  4
        14
 10
3)42
  30      10 × 3 = 30
  12
  12      4 × 3 = 12
   0
```

💬 *So the answer to the problem 42 ÷ 3 is 14.*

❹ **Show how to check the answer.**

💬 *Just to be sure, I can check to see if 14 × 3 equals 42.*

Multiply 14 × 3 on the board.

```
  4
        14              14
 10                    × 3
3)42                    42
  30      10 × 3 = 30
  12
  12      4 × 3 = 12
   0
```

💬 *So 14 is correct.*

❶ **Solve 64 ÷ 5.**

Write the long division for 64 ÷ 5 on the board.

💬 *I know that there are at least 10 groups of 5 in 64 because 10 × 5 = 50 and 50 is less than 64.*

```
   10
5)64
   50      10 × 5 = 50
   14
```

💬 *When I subtract I get 14.*

💬 *I ask myself: What number times 5 is close to 14? 2 times 5 equals 10, so I can write 2 in the quotient. Then I add 10 + 2 to figure the quotient. The remainder is 4.*

Record the long division.

```
    2
         12 R4          12
   10                   × 5
5)64                    60
   50      10 × 5 = 50  + 4
   14                   64
   10      2 × 5 = 10
    4
```

NOTICE that the gray font indicates information you have already written on the board, while the black font indicates new information to record.

❷ **Show how to check the answer.**

💬 *To check, multiply the quotient, 12, by the divisor, 5. Then add the remainder. We get 64, so 12 R4 is correct.*

CONTINUE ›

Lesson 23 **107**

Teaching With *Do The Math* **49**

Teaching Division

Clear step-by-step lessons deepen understanding by explicitly teaching students to recognize relationships between math concepts.

LESSON 23 continued **Solving division problems with partial quotients**

WHOLE GROUP

STEP 3 Elicit student responses to solve a problem.

❶ **Present a problem.**
Write the problem on the board.

$$4\overline{)52}$$

ELICIT student responses while solving a problem as part of the second phase of the gradual-release model.

❷ **Students help solve the problem.**
As you ask students the following questions, record on the board.

💬 *I don't know what number times 4 is 52, so let's begin with 10. Are there at least 10 groups of 4 in 52?* (yes)

How do you know? ($10 \times 4 = 40$ and 40 is less than 52)

How much is left? (12) *How did you figure that?* (subtracted 40 from 52)

ESTABLISH the routine of checking quotients and remainders by applying the inverse relationship of multiplication and division.

$$\begin{array}{r} 10 \\ 4\overline{)52} \\ \underline{40} \qquad 10 \times 4 = 40 \\ 12 \end{array}$$

💬 *How many 4s are there in 12?* (3)

What is 3 × 4? (12)

Record as shown.

$$\begin{array}{r} 3 \\ 10 \\ 4\overline{)52} \\ \underline{40} \qquad 10 \times 4 = 40 \\ 12 \\ \underline{12} \qquad 3 \times 4 = 12 \end{array}$$

💬 *What is the remainder?* (0)

What is the quotient? (13)

How did you get the quotient? (added 10 + 3)

Record on the board as shown.

$$\begin{array}{r} 3 \\ 10 \end{array}\!\!\diagdown\!13$$
$$\begin{array}{r} 4\overline{)52} \\ \underline{40} \qquad 10 \times 4 = 40 \\ 12 \\ \underline{12} \qquad 3 \times 4 = 12 \\ 0 \end{array}$$

❸ **Students check the answer.**
💬 *You can check to see if 13 is correct by multiplying 13 × 4 to see if it is 52.*

Have students calculate 13×4. Choose a student to record his or her multiplication on the board.

$$\begin{array}{r} 3 \\ 10 \end{array}\!\!\cdots\!13 \qquad\qquad \begin{array}{r} 13 \\ \underline{\times\, 4} \\ 52 \end{array}$$
$$\begin{array}{r} 4\overline{)52} \\ \underline{40} \qquad 10 \times 4 = 40 \\ 12 \\ \underline{12} \qquad 3 \times 4 = 12 \\ 0 \end{array}$$

108 Calculate Quotients and Remainders

Teacher Guide, Division B

PARTNERS

STEP 4
Students solve a problem.

❶ Partners solve a problem.

Have students turn to *WorkSpace* page 54.

💬 *Now you and your partner will solve the problem together, but each of you will record it on the WorkSpace page.*

Give time for students to think, pair, share to solve the problem.

❷ Record the solution.

Choose a student to tell the steps and his or her thinking as he or she solved the problem, and record on the board.

$$\begin{array}{r} 5 \\ 10 \end{array} \rightarrow 15\text{ R}1$$

4)61

$10 \times 4 = 40$

$5 \times 4 = 20$

$\begin{array}{r} 15 \\ \times 4 \\ \hline 60 \\ + 1 \\ \hline 61 \end{array}$

Have students compare their solution to the one on the board and make corrections or changes as necessary.

STEP 5
Students solve division problems.

❶ Students complete *WorkSpace* page 55.

💬 *Now you will solve some problems on your own. You may talk to your partner as you solve them or you may both wait until you are finished to compare your solutions.*

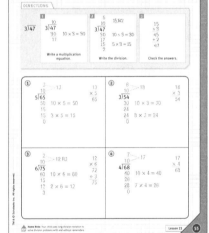

WORKSPACE PAGE 55

More Long Division Practice

SUPPORTING INSTRUCTION

Circulate around the room giving assistance as needed. If a student happens to know the answer without going through the steps, that's fine, but have him or her check the answer with multiplication.

STOP

Teaching Fractions

Intentional and careful scaffolding, along with appropriate pacing, allows students to practice new strategies before integrating them with previously learned strategies.

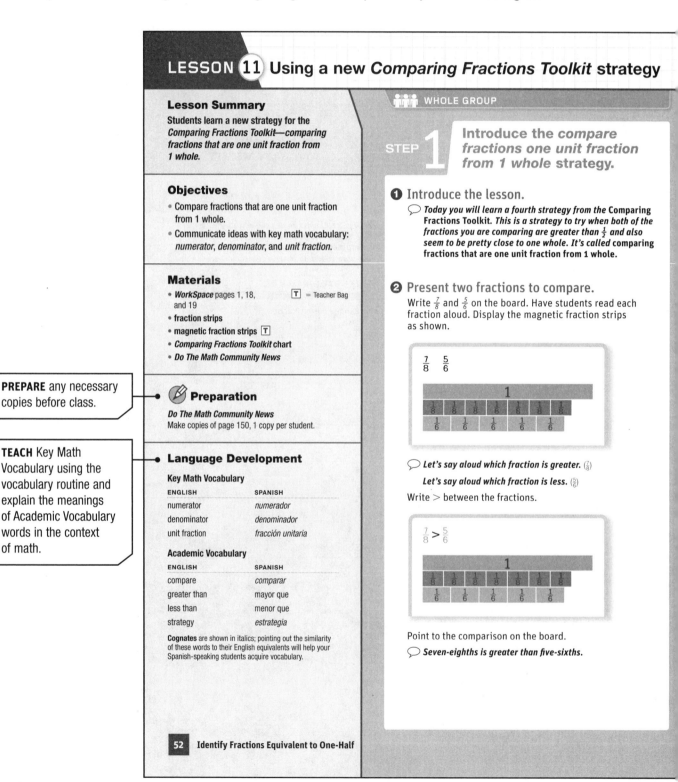

LESSON (11) Using a new *Comparing Fractions Toolkit* strategy

Lesson Summary

Students learn a new strategy for the *Comparing Fractions Toolkit*—comparing fractions that are one unit fraction from 1 whole.

Objectives

- Compare fractions that are one unit fraction from 1 whole.
- Communicate ideas with key math vocabulary: *numerator, denominator,* and *unit fraction.*

Materials

- *WorkSpace* pages 1, 18, and 19   T = Teacher Bag
- fraction strips
- magnetic fraction strips T
- *Comparing Fractions Toolkit* chart
- *Do The Math Community News*

PREPARE any necessary copies before class.

✏️ Preparation

Do The Math Community News
Make copies of page 150, 1 copy per student.

TEACH Key Math Vocabulary using the vocabulary routine and explain the meanings of Academic Vocabulary words in the context of math.

Language Development

Key Math Vocabulary

ENGLISH	SPANISH
numerator	*numerador*
denominator	*denominador*
unit fraction	*fracción unitaria*

Academic Vocabulary

ENGLISH	SPANISH
compare	*comparar*
greater than	*mayor que*
less than	*menor que*
strategy	*estrategia*

Cognates are shown in italics; pointing out the similarity of these words to their English equivalents will help your Spanish-speaking students acquire vocabulary.

52 Identify Fractions Equivalent to One-Half

👥👥👥 WHOLE GROUP

STEP 1 Introduce the *compare fractions one unit fraction from 1 whole* strategy.

❶ Introduce the lesson.

💬 *Today you will learn a fourth strategy from the* **Comparing Fractions Toolkit.** *This is a strategy to try when both of the fractions you are comparing are greater than $\frac{1}{2}$ and also seem to be pretty close to one whole. It's called comparing fractions that are one unit fraction from 1 whole.*

❷ Present two fractions to compare.

Write $\frac{7}{8}$ and $\frac{5}{6}$ on the board. Have students read each fraction aloud. Display the magnetic fraction strips as shown.

💬 *Let's say aloud which fraction is greater.* ($\frac{7}{8}$)

Let's say aloud which fraction is less. ($\frac{5}{6}$)

Write > between the fractions.

Point to the comparison on the board.

💬 *Seven-eighths is greater than five-sixths.*

Teacher Guide, Fractions B

Last Lesson Students demonstrate understanding of the objectives of Lessons 6–9.

Lesson (11) Students learn a new strategy for comparing fractions—*comparing fractions that are one unit fraction from 1 whole.*

Next Lesson Students use cube trains to learn that there are many fractions equivalent to $\frac{1}{2}$.

REVIEW how the current lesson relates to the last and next lessons.

👥 WHOLE GROUP

STEP 2

Explain how to compare fractions one unit fraction from 1 whole.

REVIEW the descriptor for each step to quickly understand the sequence of the lesson.

❶ Introduce comparing $\frac{7}{8}$ and $\frac{5}{6}$ without using fraction pieces.

💬 *We can see with the fraction pieces that the $\frac{7}{8}$ train is longer than the $\frac{5}{6}$ train, so that tells us that $\frac{7}{8}$ is greater than $\frac{5}{6}$. But suppose we didn't have our fraction pieces.*

❷ Establish that the fractions are one unit fraction less than 1 whole.

💬 *How many eighths equal 1 whole?* (8) *How many sixths equal 1 whole?* (6)

Write $1 = \frac{8}{8}$ and $1 = \frac{6}{6}$ on the board.

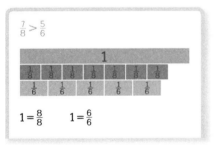

$1 = \frac{8}{8}$ $1 = \frac{6}{6}$

💬 *Let's figure how much more is needed to add on to each of the fractions to equal 1 whole.*

Use your fraction pieces to figure out the missing pieces that would make the fraction trains for $\frac{1}{8}$s and $\frac{1}{6}$s as long as the whole blue strip.

Have students think, pair, share. ($\frac{7}{8}$ is $\frac{1}{8}$ away from one whole; $\frac{5}{6}$ is $\frac{1}{6}$ away from one whole)

❸ Model with fraction strips how much to add on to make 1 whole.

Add the $\frac{1}{8}$ and $\frac{1}{6}$ magnetic fraction strips to make 1 whole. Write the equations on the board.

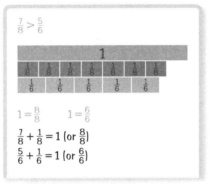

$1 = \frac{8}{8}$ $1 = \frac{6}{6}$

$\frac{7}{8} + \frac{1}{8} = 1$ (or $\frac{8}{8}$)

$\frac{5}{6} + \frac{1}{6} = 1$ (or $\frac{6}{6}$)

❹ Use the *compare unit fractions* strategy to show that $\frac{7}{8} > \frac{5}{6}$.

💬 *I know that $\frac{1}{8}$ is less than $\frac{1}{6}$. Explain how I know that.*

Have students think, pair, share. (because we can use the strategy of comparing unit fractions)

💬 *I know that $\frac{7}{8}$ is closer to one whole than $\frac{5}{6}$. Explain why.*

Have students think, pair, share. ($\frac{1}{8}$ is less than $\frac{1}{6}$, so $\frac{7}{8}$ is closer to one whole.)

💬 *Since $\frac{7}{8}$ is closer to one whole than $\frac{5}{6}$ is, $\frac{7}{8}$ has to be greater.*

ENCOURAGE partners to verify their answers and explain their thinking before "publicly" answering a question.

DISTRIBUTE the *Community News* to provide practice and reinforce skills from the previous lessons.

✏️ **Do The Math** *Community News* ✈️

Distribute the copies of the *News*.

For your convenience, a reproducible of a spinner is on the *TeacherSpace*™ CD-ROM.

This *News* provides directions for *Fraction Filler*, a game that gives students practice with fractions.

CONTINUE ▶

Lesson 11 **53**

Teaching With *Do The Math* **53**

Teaching Fractions

Each lesson contains built-in differentiation to ensure that the content is accessible to students with various needs.

FOLLOW the lesson pacing to allow time for students to practice using new strategies.

USE fraction strips to provide a concrete visual that supports the symbolic representation.

SHOW the relationship between the visual and symbolic representations.

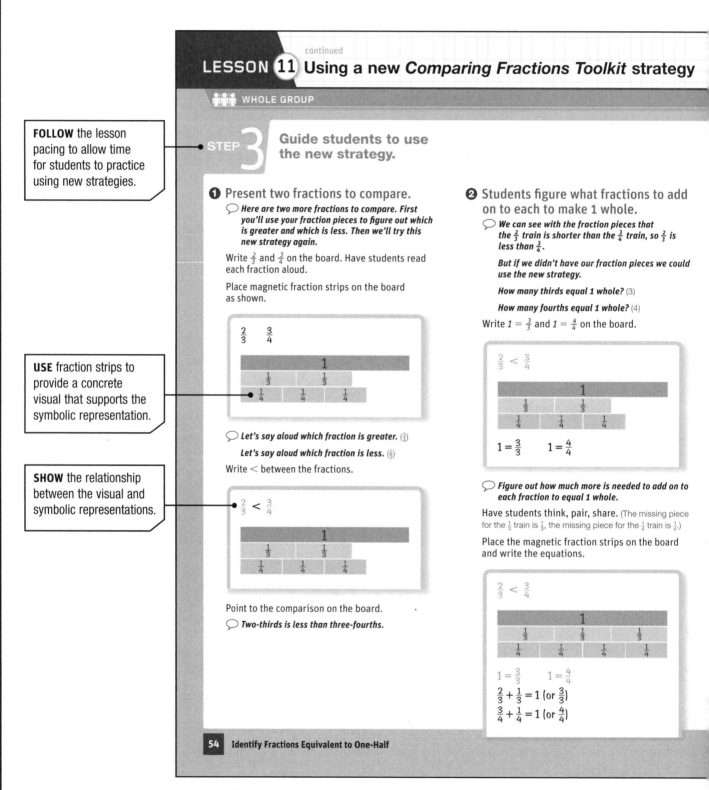

LESSON (11) continued **Using a new *Comparing Fractions Toolkit* strategy**

👥 WHOLE GROUP

STEP 3 **Guide students to use the new strategy.**

❶ **Present two fractions to compare.**

💬 *Here are two more fractions to compare. First you'll use your fraction pieces to figure out which is greater and which is less. Then we'll try this new strategy again.*

Write $\frac{2}{3}$ and $\frac{3}{4}$ on the board. Have students read each fraction aloud.

Place magnetic fraction strips on the board as shown.

$\frac{2}{3}$ $\frac{3}{4}$

| 1 |
| $\frac{1}{3}$ | $\frac{1}{3}$ |
| $\frac{1}{4}$ | $\frac{1}{4}$ | $\frac{1}{4}$ |

💬 *Let's say aloud which fraction is greater.* $(\frac{3}{4})$

Let's say aloud which fraction is less. $(\frac{2}{3})$

Write $<$ between the fractions.

$\frac{2}{3} < \frac{3}{4}$

| 1 |
| $\frac{1}{3}$ | $\frac{1}{3}$ |
| $\frac{1}{4}$ | $\frac{1}{4}$ | $\frac{1}{4}$ |

Point to the comparison on the board.

💬 *Two-thirds is less than three-fourths.*

❷ **Students figure what fractions to add on to each to make 1 whole.**

💬 *We can see with the fraction pieces that the $\frac{2}{3}$ train is shorter than the $\frac{3}{4}$ train, so $\frac{2}{3}$ is less than $\frac{3}{4}$.*

But if we didn't have our fraction pieces we could use the new strategy.

How many thirds equal 1 whole? (3)

How many fourths equal 1 whole? (4)

Write $1 = \frac{3}{3}$ and $1 = \frac{4}{4}$ on the board.

$\frac{2}{3} < \frac{3}{4}$

| 1 |
| $\frac{1}{3}$ | $\frac{1}{3}$ |
| $\frac{1}{4}$ | $\frac{1}{4}$ | $\frac{1}{4}$ |

$1 = \frac{3}{3}$ $1 = \frac{4}{4}$

💬 *Figure out how much more is needed to add on to each fraction to equal 1 whole.*

Have students think, pair, share. (The missing piece for the $\frac{1}{3}$ train is $\frac{1}{3}$, the missing piece for the $\frac{1}{4}$ train is $\frac{1}{4}$.)

Place the magnetic fraction strips on the board and write the equations.

$\frac{2}{3} < \frac{3}{4}$

| 1 |
| $\frac{1}{3}$ | $\frac{1}{3}$ | $\frac{1}{3}$ |
| $\frac{1}{4}$ | $\frac{1}{4}$ | $\frac{1}{4}$ | $\frac{1}{4}$ |

$1 = \frac{3}{3}$ $1 = \frac{4}{4}$

$\frac{2}{3} + \frac{1}{3} = 1$ (or $\frac{3}{3}$)

$\frac{3}{4} + \frac{1}{4} = 1$ (or $\frac{4}{4}$)

54 Identify Fractions Equivalent to One-Half

Teacher Guide, Fractions B

👤 INDIVIDUALS

❸ Students explain why $\frac{2}{3} < \frac{3}{4}$.

💬 *Explain how you know that $\frac{1}{4}$ is less than $\frac{1}{3}$.*

Have students think, pair, share. (Because we can use the strategy of comparing unit fractions.)

💬 *Explain how we know that $\frac{3}{4}$ has to be closer to 1 whole.*

Have students think, pair, share. ($\frac{1}{4}$ is less than $\frac{1}{3}$, so $\frac{3}{4}$ is closer to one whole.)

💬 *Explain why $\frac{3}{4}$ has to be greater than $\frac{2}{3}$.*

Have students think, pair, share. ($\frac{1}{4}$ is a smaller piece taken from the whole, leaving more of the whole remaining.)

Choose students to explain the strategy in their own words.

❹ Write the strategy on the chart.

Comparing Fractions Toolkit

Strategy 1: compare unit fractions
$\frac{1}{2} > \frac{1}{8}$

Strategy 2: compare fractions with common numerators
$\frac{3}{12} < \frac{3}{4}$

Strategy 3: compare fractions with common denominators
$\frac{1}{4} < \frac{2}{4}$

Strategy 4: compare fractions one unit fraction from 1 whole
$\frac{7}{8} > \frac{5}{6}$

Have students read the strategy on *WorkSpace* page 1.

STEP 4 — Students practice the new strategy.

❶ **Students complete *WorkSpace* page 18.**

Have students turn to page 18. Explain that they will compare two fractions using their fraction pieces and fill in each equation with the missing fraction that will make it equal to 1 whole.

❷ **Partners check with each other.**

When students have filled in < or > and completed the equations, have them check with their partners to see if they agree. If not, they should recheck with their fraction pieces.

❸ **Students complete *WorkSpace* page 19.**

Students practice using all four toolkit strategies.

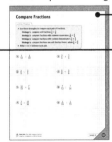

STOP

ENCOURAGE students to confer with each other as they complete *WorkSpace* assignments.

CHECK for understanding as students apply strategies in the *WorkSpace*.

ADD strategies to a cumulative chart for students to use as a reference for solving new problems.

Using Children's Literature to Teach Math

Each of the twelve *Do The Math* modules includes two copies of at least one read-aloud book to support the math concepts in a meaningful context.

Addition & Subtraction B

Division B

Multiplication B

Fractions B

Read Alouds In Action

Read alouds provide a springboard and context for instruction and support with new math content in an engaging and accessible format. Follow the instructions in the Teacher Guide, as they vary from module to module.

For example, follow this procedure to provide a context for learning about square numbers with *Bats on Parade* in Multiplication B:

❶ Introduce the lesson by previewing the book you are going to read aloud.

❷ Show students the cover of the book and read the title, author's name, and illustrator's name.

❸ Read the book aloud, showing the illustrations on each page.

❹ Reread the book two pages at a time, pausing to focus on the equations.

❺ Demonstrate how to arrange tiles to match the bat formations in the book.

❻ Refer back to the illustrations in the book as students model the equations with tiles and drawings.

Reflecting on Using Read Alouds in Math

Bats on Parade by Kathi Appelt provides a context for investigating the multiplication pattern of square numbers up to 100. Listen to a section of the read-aloud book and watch a teacher revisit it with her students.

Video Reflection

How did the teacher connect the read aloud to the math concept?

_____

_____

_____

_____

_____

How did the teacher build understanding of square numbers?

_____

_____

_____

_____

_____

My Experience

How is this approach different from how you learned about square numbers?

_____

_____

_____

_____

_____

TEACHER TIP

Display the extra copy of the read aloud in the classroom library so that students can reread it independently.

Using Manipulatives to Teach Math

Using concrete materials to represent abstract mathematical ideas gives students a chance to build number sense, develop skills, and deepen their mathematical understanding.

> 66 The materials help students get their hands on abstract ideas and help them form the mental models they need to build understanding. 99
>
> —Marilyn Burns

Manipulatives in the Classroom

Students use manipulatives throughout the *Do The Math* lessons to build their mathematical understanding. Explicit connections between the concrete materials and the abstract representation make the content accessible to all students.

The storage bags facilitate the distribution and management of hands-on materials. Each module includes four red mesh bags of Student Pair Materials that store the manipulatives needed for four pairs of students and one Teacher Demonstration Materials bag, containing all the concrete materials needed for instruction.

In *Do The Math*:

■ Students connect the manipulative model to the abstract representation.

■ Students use manipulatives for support as they work with new concepts in pairs or independently.

■ Students gain confidence as they build their understanding of the math content.

Manipulatives In Action

Follow the instructions in your Teacher Guide when using hands-on materials. Consider these suggestions when introducing manipulatives to your students:

■ Clearly state that manipulatives are to be used for mathematical purposes only.

■ Store the bags of manipulatives in an accessible area and determine a consistent routine for their distribution.

■ Remind students to return all manipulatives to their storage bags when they finish, and verify all materials have been collected at the end of the lesson.

■ Post a reference chart for students with the name of each manipulative and a description of its use.

■ Involve families by introducing them to the benefits of manipulatives during Back to School Night.

Reflecting on Using Manipulatives

After watching a teacher use tiles to demonstrate how to solve division problems with remainders, think about how these hands-on materials help students better understand the math concepts.

Video Reflection

What steps did the teacher in the video take when using manipulatives to solve division problems?

_____

_____

_____

_____

_____

What made this lesson effective?

_____

_____

_____

_____

_____

My Experience

How did this lesson differ from how you usually teach division with remainders?

_____

_____

_____

_____

TEACHER TIP

When you introduce new manipulatives, allow time for free exploration. After students interact with the manipulatives for a few minutes, they will be ready to use them for math purposes.

Using Games to Teach and Practice Math

Do The Math modules include games to provide students with meaningful practice to deepen their understanding of new math concepts and increase their computational proficiency.

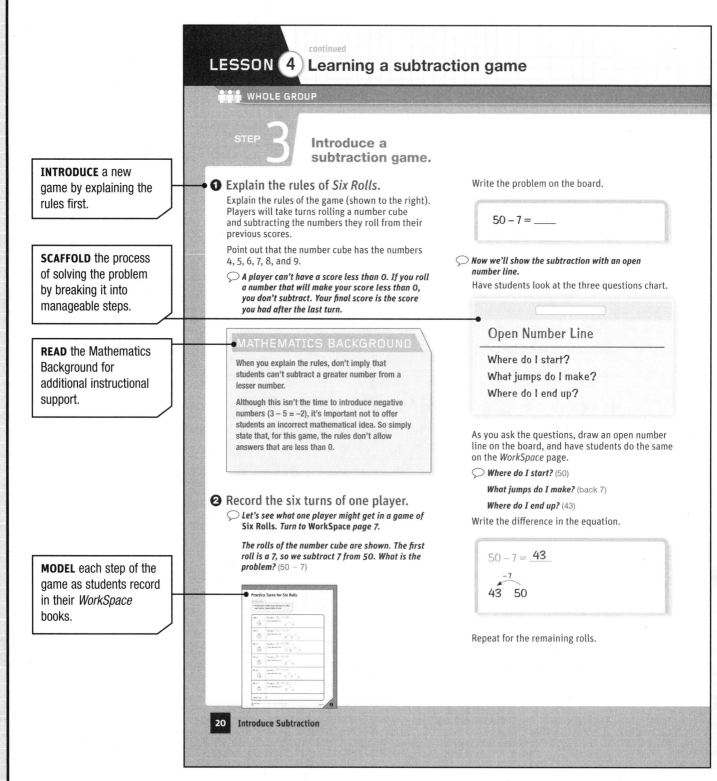

INTRODUCE a new game by explaining the rules first.

SCAFFOLD the process of solving the problem by breaking it into manageable steps.

READ the Mathematics Background for additional instructional support.

MODEL each step of the game as students record in their *WorkSpace* books.

---

continued

LESSON **4** Learning a subtraction game

👥👥👥 WHOLE GROUP

STEP **3** Introduce a subtraction game.

❶ **Explain the rules of *Six Rolls*.**

Explain the rules of the game (shown to the right). Players will take turns rolling a number cube and subtracting the numbers they roll from their previous scores.

Point out that the number cube has the numbers 4, 5, 6, 7, 8, and 9.

💬 *A player can't have a score less than 0. If you roll a number that will make your score less than 0, you don't subtract. Your final score is the score you had after the last turn.*

MATHEMATICS BACKGROUND

When you explain the rules, don't imply that students can't subtract a greater number from a lesser number.

Although this isn't the time to introduce negative numbers ($3 - 5 = -2$), it's important not to offer students an incorrect mathematical idea. So simply state that, for this game, the rules don't allow answers that are less than 0.

❷ **Record the six turns of one player.**

💬 *Let's see what one player might get in a game of Six Rolls. Turn to WorkSpace page 7.*

The rolls of the number cube are shown. The first roll is a 7, so we subtract 7 from 50. What is the problem? (50 − 7)

20 Introduce Subtraction

Write the problem on the board.

$$50 - 7 = \underline{\quad}$$

💬 *Now we'll show the subtraction with an open number line.*

Have students look at the three questions chart.

Open Number Line

Where do I start?

What jumps do I make?

Where do I end up?

As you ask the questions, draw an open number line on the board, and have students do the same on the *WorkSpace* page.

💬 *Where do I start?* (50)

What jumps do I make? (back 7)

Where do I end up? (43)

Write the difference in the equation.

$$50 - 7 = \underline{43}$$

43   50 (−7)

Repeat for the remaining rolls.

Teacher Guide, Addition & Subtraction B

Playing a Subtraction Game

Watch a video of a teacher modeling the *Six Rolls* game for students. Then, play the game with a partner.

Six Rolls

Player A		Player B	
Roll 1 ____	Equation _____ Open Number Line	Roll 1 ____	Equation _____ Open Number Line
Roll 2 ____	Equation _____ Open Number Line	Roll 2 ____	Equation _____ Open Number Line
Roll 3 ____	Equation _____ Open Number Line	Roll 3 ____	Equation _____ Open Number Line
Roll 4 ____	Equation _____ Open Number Line	Roll 4 ____	Equation _____ Open Number Line
Roll 5 ____	Equation _____ Open Number Line	Roll 5 ____	Equation _____ Open Number Line
Roll 6 ____	Equation _____ Open Number Line	Roll 6 ____	Equation _____ Open Number Line
Final Score ____		Final Score ____	

Home Note: Your child practices subtracting one-digit numbers from two-digit numbers by playing a game.

Lesson 4

9

WorkSpace, Addition & Subtraction B

Teaching Math Vocabulary

After students experience the math content firsthand, follow a consistent instructional routine to explicitly teach new math terms.

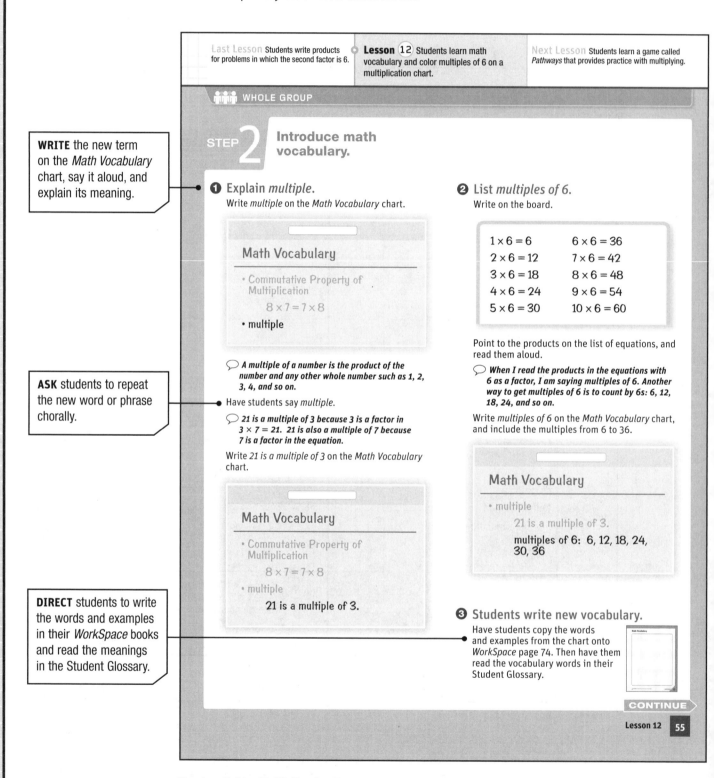

Last Lesson Students write products for problems in which the second factor is 6.

Lesson 12 Students learn math vocabulary and color multiples of 6 on a multiplication chart.

Next Lesson Students learn a game called *Pathways* that provides practice with multiplying.

👥👥👥 WHOLE GROUP

STEP 2 Introduce math vocabulary.

WRITE the new term on the *Math Vocabulary* chart, say it aloud, and explain its meaning.

❶ Explain *multiple*.
Write *multiple* on the *Math Vocabulary* chart.

Math Vocabulary
- Commutative Property of Multiplication
  $8 \times 7 = 7 \times 8$
- multiple

💬 *A multiple of a number is the product of the number and any other whole number such as 1, 2, 3, 4, and so on.*

Have students say *multiple*.

💬 *21 is a multiple of 3 because 3 is a factor in $3 \times 7 = 21$. 21 is also a multiple of 7 because 7 is a factor in the equation.*

Write *21 is a multiple of 3* on the *Math Vocabulary* chart.

ASK students to repeat the new word or phrase chorally.

Math Vocabulary
- Commutative Property of Multiplication
  $8 \times 7 = 7 \times 8$
- multiple
  21 is a multiple of 3.

DIRECT students to write the words and examples in their *WorkSpace* books and read the meanings in the Student Glossary.

❷ List *multiples of 6*.
Write on the board.

$1 \times 6 = 6$	$6 \times 6 = 36$
$2 \times 6 = 12$	$7 \times 6 = 42$
$3 \times 6 = 18$	$8 \times 6 = 48$
$4 \times 6 = 24$	$9 \times 6 = 54$
$5 \times 6 = 30$	$10 \times 6 = 60$

Point to the products on the list of equations, and read them aloud.

💬 *When I read the products in the equations with 6 as a factor, I am saying multiples of 6. Another way to get multiples of 6 is to count by 6s: 6, 12, 18, 24, and so on.*

Write *multiples of 6* on the *Math Vocabulary* chart, and include the multiples from 6 to 36.

Math Vocabulary
- multiple
  21 is a multiple of 3.
  multiples of 6: 6, 12, 18, 24, 30, 36

❸ Students write new vocabulary.
Have students copy the words and examples from the chart onto *WorkSpace* page 74. Then have them read the vocabulary words in their Student Glossary.

CONTINUE ▶

Lesson 12 **55**

Teacher Guide, Multiplication B

Reflecting on Teaching Math Terms

Watch a teacher model the vocabulary instruction routine. Then briefly describe each step below.

❶ **See It** _____

_____

❷ **Hear It** _____

_____

❸ **Say It** _____

_____

❹ **Write It** _____

_____

❺ **Read It** _____

_____

> ❝ The purpose of the language of mathematics is communicating about mathematical ideas, and it's necessary first to acquire knowledge about the ideas that the mathematical language describes. ❞
>
> **—Marilyn Burns**

What do you find effective about the vocabulary instruction routine?

_____

_____

_____

List any questions you still have about explicit vocabulary instruction in math.

_____

_____

_____

TEACHER TIP

Help students remember new math terms by having them restate the meanings to a partner. Reinforce their understanding by providing multiple opportunities for students to use the new words in context.

Notes

Measuring Growth

Each Teacher Guide contains a Beginning-of-Module Assessment and an End-of-Module Assessment to measure students' growth in math proficiency for that topic.

Beginning-of-Module Assessment

Establish baseline scores with the Beginning-of-Module Assessment. Use the Assessment Answers page to determine scores.

- Students who cannot correctly answer the first few problems of the assessment do not have the prerequisite skills needed to start work in this module.

- Students who score 80 percent or higher are proficient in the skills taught for this module topic.

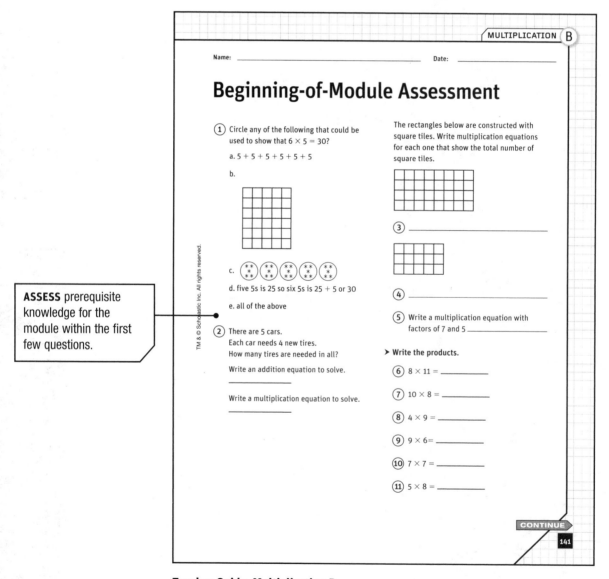

> **ASSESS** prerequisite knowledge for the module within the first few questions.

Within the assessment sheet:

MULTIPLICATION B

Name: _____ Date: _____

Beginning-of-Module Assessment

1. Circle any of the following that could be used to show that $6 \times 5 = 30$?

   a. $5 + 5 + 5 + 5 + 5 + 5$

   b.

   c.

   d. five 5s is 25 so six 5s is $25 + 5$ or 30

   e. all of the above

2. There are 5 cars.
   Each car needs 4 new tires.
   How many tires are needed in all?

   Write an addition equation to solve.
   _____

   Write a multiplication equation to solve.
   _____

The rectangles below are constructed with square tiles. Write multiplication equations for each one that show the total number of square tiles.

3. _____

4. _____

5. Write a multiplication equation with factors of 7 and 5 _____

➤ Write the products.

6. $8 \times 11 =$ _____

7. $10 \times 8 =$ _____

8. $4 \times 9 =$ _____

9. $9 \times 6 =$ _____

10. $7 \times 7 =$ _____

11. $5 \times 8 =$ _____

CONTINUE

141

Teacher Guide, Multiplication B

End-of-Module Assessment

Administer the End-of-Module Assessment after teaching the 30 lessons in a module. Compare students' End-of-Module Assessment scores to their baseline scores to measure growth for that topic.

- Students scoring 80 percent or higher have demonstrated proficiency in the module objectives.

- Students scoring below 80 percent need additional support and practice with these concepts and skills to become proficient.

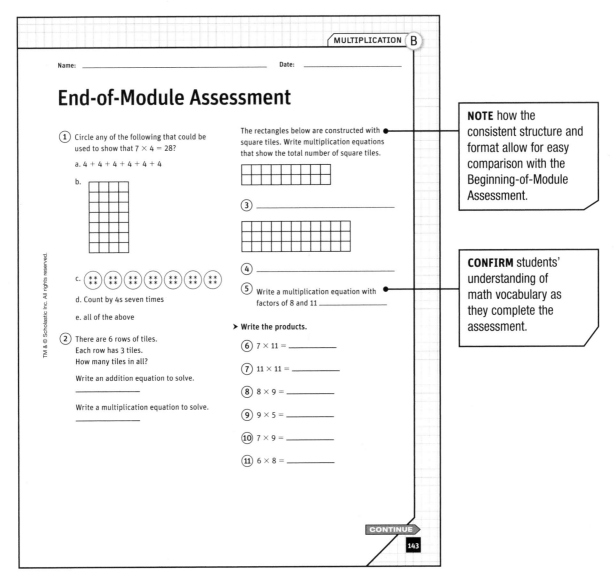

NOTE how the consistent structure and format allow for easy comparison with the Beginning-of-Module Assessment.

CONFIRM students' understanding of math vocabulary as they complete the assessment.

Teacher Guide, Multiplication B

Print multiple copies of the assessments and answer pages for the topic.

Monitoring Progress

There are opportunities for assessment throughout the *Do The Math* modules. Use what you learn from students' responses to differentiate instruction and monitor progress.

Assess Student Understanding

During every fifth lesson, students independently complete the Show What You Know page in the *WorkSpace* to demonstrate understanding of the math content from the previous four lessons.

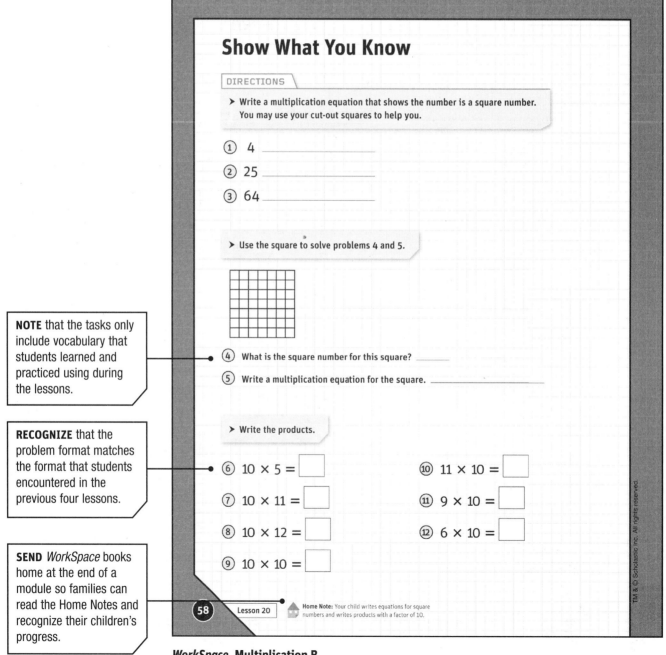

Show What You Know

> DIRECTIONS

> Write a multiplication equation that shows the number is a square number. You may use your cut-out squares to help you.

① 4 _____

② 25 _____

③ 64 _____

> Use the square to solve problems 4 and 5.

④ What is the square number for this square? _____

⑤ Write a multiplication equation for the square. _____

> Write the products.

⑥ $10 \times 5 =$ ☐

⑦ $10 \times 11 =$ ☐

⑧ $10 \times 12 =$ ☐

⑨ $10 \times 10 =$ ☐

⑩ $11 \times 10 =$ ☐

⑪ $9 \times 10 =$ ☐

⑫ $6 \times 10 =$ ☐

58   Lesson 20   **Home Note:** Your child writes equations for square numbers and writes products with a factor of 10.

NOTE that the tasks only include vocabulary that students learned and practiced using during the lessons.

RECOGNIZE that the problem format matches the format that students encountered in the previous four lessons.

SEND *WorkSpace* books home at the end of a module so families can read the Home Notes and recognize their children's progress.

WorkSpace, **Multiplication B**

Differentiate Instruction

After students complete the *WorkSpace* assessment, use the Progress Monitoring suggestions to differentiate instruction and provide additional support, practice, or challenge.

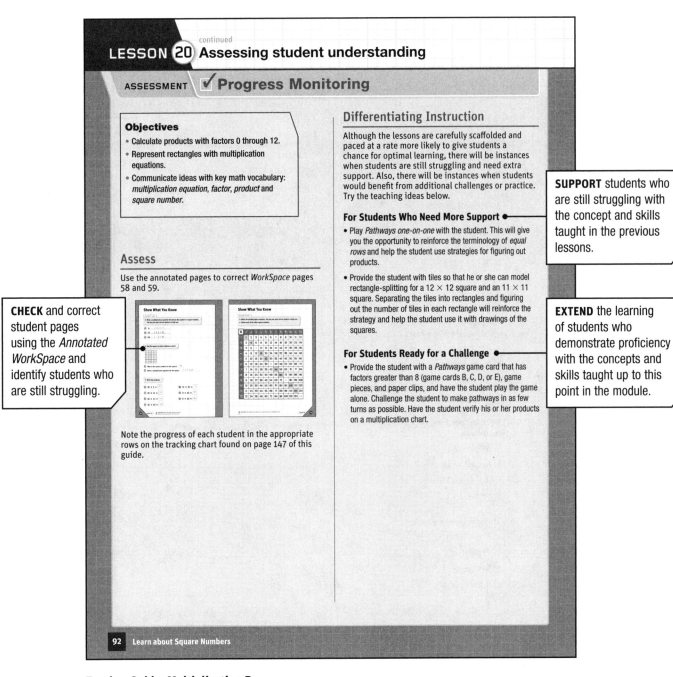

LESSON 20 continued **Assessing student understanding**

ASSESSMENT ☑ **Progress Monitoring**

Objectives
- Calculate products with factors 0 through 12.
- Represent rectangles with multiplication equations.
- Communicate ideas with key math vocabulary: *multiplication equation, factor, product* and *square number.*

Assess

Use the annotated pages to correct *WorkSpace* pages 58 and 59.

CHECK and correct student pages using the *Annotated WorkSpace* and identify students who are still struggling.

Note the progress of each student in the appropriate rows on the tracking chart found on page 147 of this guide.

Differentiating Instruction

Although the lessons are carefully scaffolded and paced at a rate more likely to give students a chance for optimal learning, there will be instances when students are still struggling and need extra support. Also, there will be instances when students would benefit from additional challenges or practice. Try the teaching ideas below.

For Students Who Need More Support ●
- Play *Pathways one-on-one* with the student. This will give you the opportunity to reinforce the terminology of *equal rows* and help the student use strategies for figuring out products.
- Provide the student with tiles so that he or she can model rectangle-splitting for a 12 × 12 square and an 11 × 11 square. Separating the tiles into rectangles and figuring out the number of tiles in each rectangle will reinforce the strategy and help the student use it with drawings of the squares.

For Students Ready for a Challenge ●
- Provide the student with a *Pathways* game card that has factors greater than 8 (game cards B, C, D, or E), game pieces, and paper clips, and have the student play the game alone. Challenge the student to make pathways in as few turns as possible. Have the student verify his or her products on a multiplication chart.

SUPPORT students who are still struggling with the concept and skills taught in the previous lessons.

EXTEND the learning of students who demonstrate proficiency with the concepts and skills taught up to this point in the module.

92 Learn about Square Numbers

Teacher Guide, Multiplication B

Surveying Students

Students who struggle with math tend to dislike it. Survey students and compare their attitudes toward math before and after teaching a *Do The Math* module.

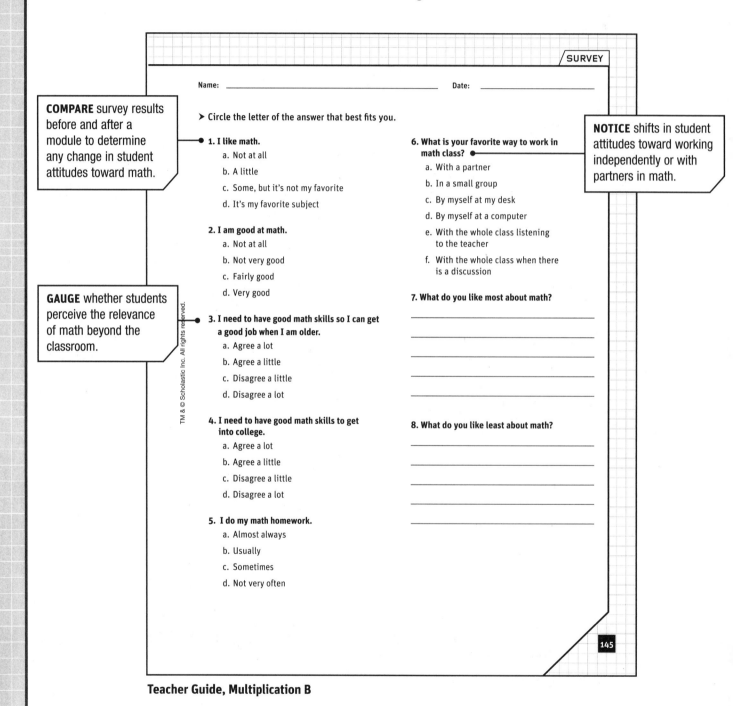

COMPARE survey results before and after a module to determine any change in student attitudes toward math.

GAUGE whether students perceive the relevance of math beyond the classroom.

NOTICE shifts in student attitudes toward working independently or with partners in math.

/ SURVEY

Name: _____   Date: _____

➤ Circle the letter of the answer that best fits you.

1. I like math.
   a. Not at all
   b. A little
   c. Some, but it's not my favorite
   d. It's my favorite subject

2. I am good at math.
   a. Not at all
   b. Not very good
   c. Fairly good
   d. Very good

3. I need to have good math skills so I can get a good job when I am older.
   a. Agree a lot
   b. Agree a little
   c. Disagree a little
   d. Disagree a lot

4. I need to have good math skills to get into college.
   a. Agree a lot
   b. Agree a little
   c. Disagree a little
   d. Disagree a lot

5. I do my math homework.
   a. Almost always
   b. Usually
   c. Sometimes
   d. Not very often

6. What is your favorite way to work in math class?
   a. With a partner
   b. In a small group
   c. By myself at my desk
   d. By myself at a computer
   e. With the whole class listening to the teacher
   f. With the whole class when there is a discussion

7. What do you like most about math?
   _____
   _____
   _____
   _____
   _____

8. What do you like least about math?
   _____
   _____
   _____
   _____

145

Teacher Guide, Multiplication B

Tracking Objectives

Track and record student progress toward meeting the objectives of each module.

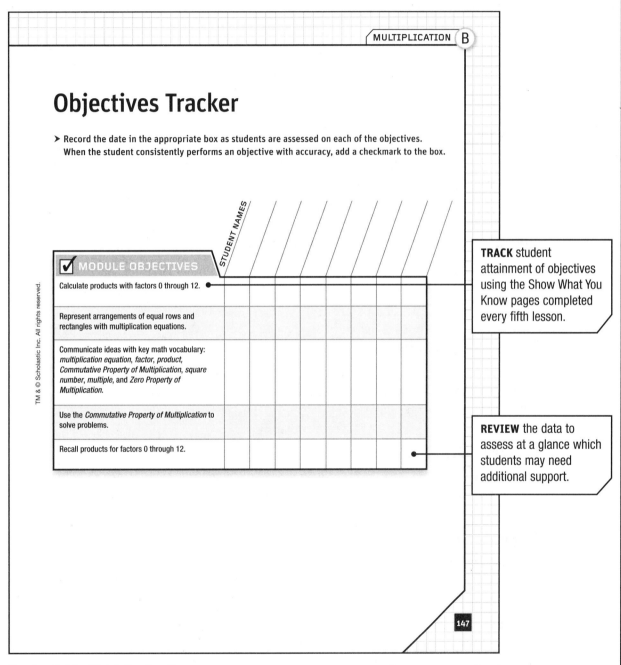

MULTIPLICATION B

Objectives Tracker

➤ Record the date in the appropriate box as students are assessed on each of the objectives. When the student consistently performs an objective with accuracy, add a checkmark to the box.

☑ MODULE OBJECTIVES	STUDENT NAMES							
Calculate products with factors 0 through 12.								
Represent arrangements of equal rows and rectangles with multiplication equations.								
Communicate ideas with key math vocabulary: *multiplication equation, factor, product, Commutative Property of Multiplication, square number, multiple,* and *Zero Property of Multiplication.*								
Use the *Commutative Property of Multiplication* to solve problems.								
Recall products for factors 0 through 12.								

TRACK student attainment of objectives using the Show What You Know pages completed every fifth lesson.

REVIEW the data to assess at a glance which students may need additional support.

147

Teacher Guide, Multiplication B

TEACHER TIP

Keep folders with copies of assessments, surveys, and Objectives Trackers to reference during student and parent conferences.

Supporting English Learners

Do The Math incorporates various supports throughout the program to ensure maximum accessibility to English language learners.

Built-In Differentiation

Suggestions on the planner pages highlight important key practices that support English language learners.

Visual Directions

Pictures accompany the step-by-step directions so that students connect verbal and written directions with images. In this way, students can access the math content without encountering additional language demands.

Intentional Vocabulary Instruction

Students learn new terms following a consistent instructional routine—*see it*, *hear it*, *say it*, *write it*, and *read it*—so they can effectively use the math vocabulary when communicating about their learning.

Spanish Language Support

Spanish translations of key math and academic vocabulary terms and Spanish cognates enable teachers to support Spanish-speaking students as they acquire the language of math in English.

Graphic Organizers

Graphic organizers, such as concept webs, provide visual representations to help students make strong connections between the math concepts and vocabulary terms.

Read Alouds

Children's books provide opportunities to develop language skills as students listen to the teacher read aloud and connect the pictures to the language and math concepts.

Manipulatives and Games

These high-interest strategies allow students to engage in mathematical learning through hands-on nonverbal representations of concepts.

Think, Pair, Share

Think, Pair, Share is a routine that allows student pairs to interact in a safe environment as they compare solutions, make corrections, discuss errors, and rehearse ideas before addressing the larger group.

Placing Students in *Do The Math*

Before implementing *Do The Math*, decide how the program can best meet your students' needs.

Students Needing In-Class Intervention

For students struggling with grade-level work, teach a *Do The Math* module to establish foundational knowledge before studying a math topic in the textbook.

- If previewing a topic from your textbook would benefit all of your students, teach *Do The Math* to the whole class.

- If several of your students are struggling with grade-level work, teach *Do The Math* to a small group while other students work independently on computers, math activities, or class work.

Students One Year Below Grade Level

Examine student records and test scores to identify students who are one year below grade level.

- Refer to the chart on page 75 to help select a *Do The Math* module that correlates with math concepts from the previous year.

- Teach the selected *Do The Math* module(s) during small-group instruction, after school, or in summer school.

Students Two Years Below Grade Level

Students with test scores significantly below grade level may need intervention with a specialist, such as a Title I teacher, math intervention instructor, or special education teacher. Work with the specialist to select the appropriate modules and to determine the best intervention model.

- **Push-In Intervention:** Small-group instruction of *Do The Math* with a specialist in the main classroom

- **Pull-Out Intervention:** Scheduled intervention instruction of *Do The Math* with a specialist in a different classroom

- **Intervention Class:** An elective period for middle school students taught by a teacher who specializes in intervention

- **Summer School:** Intensive instruction with an intervention specialist over the summer to prepare students for grade-level math in the upcoming school year

Do The Math In-Class Intervention Alignment

30-min/day	6 Weeks	6 Weeks	6 Weeks
Grade 2	Addition & Subtraction Ⓐ	Addition & Subtraction Ⓑ	Addition & Subtraction Ⓒ
Grade 3	Multiplication Ⓐ	Multiplication Ⓑ	Division Ⓐ
Grade 4	Multiplication Ⓒ	Division Ⓑ	Fractions Ⓐ
Grade 5	Division Ⓒ	Fractions Ⓑ	Fractions Ⓒ

Developing an Implementation Plan

Use these questions to decide how to implement *Do The Math* in your classroom.

Think About...	In My Classroom...
How many students are in your class?	
How many students would benefit from *Do The Math* for support with grade-level math?	
How many students in your class are one year below grade level in math?	
How many students are two or more years below grade level and require specialized intervention?	
Do you plan to teach *Do The Math* with the whole class or a small group?	
When in your schedule will you teach 30 minutes of *Do The Math* every day?	
If you plan to teach *Do The Math* with a small group, what are some of the independent activities that the rest of the class can do?	

Connecting School to Home

Use *Do The Math Community News* to keep families and regular classroom teachers informed of student learning. The suggested games and activities encourage family involvement and provide students with additional practice.

INFORM families of the *Do The Math* module topic that students are studying.

PROVIDE clear directions for math games that students can play with their families at home.

UPDATE families by sending home the *Community News* after every group of five lessons.

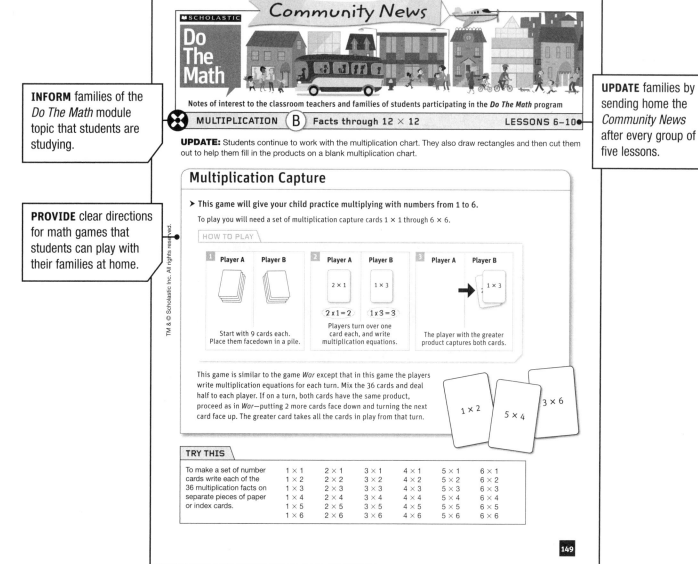

Community News

SCHOLASTIC

Do The Math

Notes of interest to the classroom teachers and families of students participating in the *Do The Math* program

MULTIPLICATION (B) Facts through 12 × 12   LESSONS 6–10

UPDATE: Students continue to work with the multiplication chart. They also draw rectangles and then cut them out to help them fill in the products on a blank multiplication chart.

Multiplication Capture

➤ This game will give your child practice multiplying with numbers from 1 to 6.

To play you will need a set of multiplication capture cards 1 × 1 through 6 × 6.

HOW TO PLAY

1. **Player A** **Player B**
Start with 9 cards each. Place them facedown in a pile.

2. **Player A** **Player B**
2 × 1   1 × 3
2 x 1 = 2   1 x 3 = 3
Players turn over one card each, and write multiplication equations.

3. **Player A** **Player B**
1 × 3
The player with the greater product captures both cards.

This game is similar to the game *War* except that in this game the players write multiplication equations for each turn. Mix the 36 cards and deal half to each player. If on a turn, both cards have the same product, proceed as in *War*—putting 2 more cards face down and turning the next card face up. The greater card takes all the cards in play from that turn.

1 × 2   5 × 4   3 × 6

TRY THIS

To make a set of number cards write each of the 36 multiplication facts on separate pieces of paper or index cards.					
1 × 1	2 × 1	3 × 1	4 × 1	5 × 1	6 × 1
1 × 2	2 × 2	3 × 2	4 × 2	5 × 2	6 × 2
1 × 3	2 × 3	3 × 3	4 × 3	5 × 3	6 × 3
1 × 4	2 × 4	3 × 4	4 × 4	5 × 4	6 × 4
1 × 5	2 × 5	3 × 5	4 × 5	5 × 5	6 × 5
1 × 6	2 × 6	3 × 6	4 × 6	5 × 6	6 × 6

149

Teacher Guide, Multiplication B

Print a Spanish translation of the *Community News* to send home to Spanish-speaking families.

Notes

Continuing Your Learning

Scholastic and Math Solutions Professional Development have collaborated to provide a selection of professional opportunities to support *Do The Math* teachers.

Implementation Training

This half-day training provides an overview of *Do The Math* and hands-on experience with the program to get started with implementation.

Embedded Professional Learning

The following components of *Do The Math* provide comprehensive support for teachers using the program:

- Carefully paced and scaffolded lessons with embedded instructional support and differentiation strategies

- *TeacherSpace* binder to organize professional materials and the CD-ROM with videos, reproducibles, and professional articles

- *Teaching Arithmetic* series by Marilyn Burns with pedagogical support

Professional Development Partnership

Founded by Marilyn Burns, Math Solutions Professional Development has served school districts nationwide for nearly 25 years. Scholastic is pleased to collaborate with Math Solutions to offer professional development options for *Do The Math* teachers. All of the options introduce the components of *Do The Math*.

Choose the option that best addresses your school or district's specific needs:

Two-Day Introductory Course provides the essentials teachers need to begin implementation of *Do The Math*.

Five-Day School-Year Series links to ongoing implementation of *Do The Math* and provides ongoing feedback to teachers during the implementation of the program.

Five-Day Immersion Summer Course provides pedagogical background and in-depth experiences with program content and instructional practices.

For more information, contact Math Solutions at 800-868-9092 or visit www.mathsolutions.com.

Exploring *TeacherSpace*

Each of the four topic areas includes a *TeacherSpace* CD-ROM with assessments, professional articles, reproducibles, *Community News*, and model videos.

TeacherSpace, **Multiplication**

About *TeacherSpace*™ provides a brief description of the features of the *TeacherSpace* CD-ROM.

Video Clips include videos of teachers demonstrating *Do The Math* strategies in model classrooms and keynotes from Marilyn Burns explaining the challenges of the topic area and the highlights of the modules.

Professional Articles by Marilyn Burns are available through a link to the Math Solutions® Professional Development Web site.

Reproducibles contain Beginning- and End-of-Module Assessments, games directions, and the *Community News* in English and Spanish.

***Do The Math* Community** links to the *Do The Math* Community Web site at www.scholastic.com/dothemath/community with best practices and teacher tips.

Exploring Math Solutions

Math Solutions is dedicated to improving and strengthening standards-based instruction through books, professional articles, and on-site courses. Its Web site is an essential resource for teachers and administrators looking to enrich their understanding of math instruction. Visit www.mathsolutions.com to learn more.

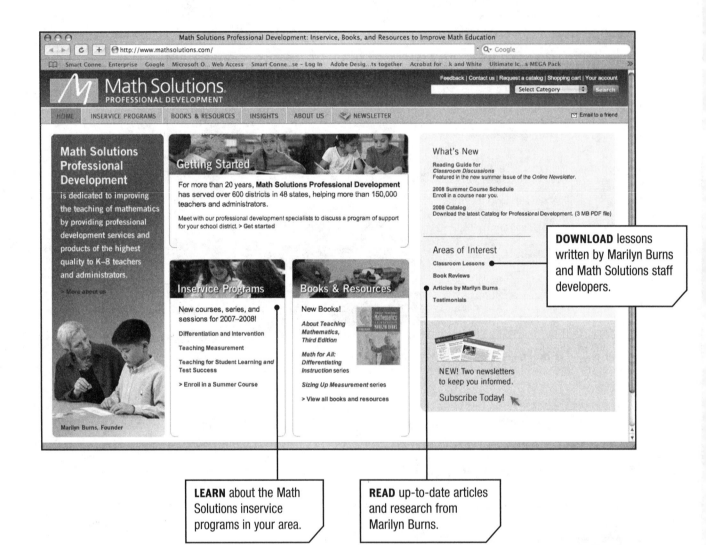

DOWNLOAD lessons written by Marilyn Burns and Math Solutions staff developers.

LEARN about the Math Solutions inservice programs in your area.

READ up-to-date articles and research from Marilyn Burns.

Looking at How Students Reason

Mathematics teachers gain a wealth of information by delving into the thinking behind students' answers, not just when answers are wrong but also when they are correct.

by Marilyn Burns

First, a confession: Only during the last 10 to 15 years of my teaching career have I thought deeply about assessing students' understanding and learning progress. As a beginning teacher, I focused on learning to manage my classroom, plan lessons, and hold students' attention. Later, my focus shifted to improving my lessons and expanding my instructional repertoire. During those years, my attention was always firmly on my teaching. Assessment was not one of my concerns. Yes, I gave assignments and quizzes and examined the results, but I did so more to determine grades than to figure out what students were thinking.

Assessment plays a much different role in my teaching today. Although I'm no longer a full-time classroom teacher, I still spend time teaching students in elementary classrooms as I try out new instructional ideas. I now approach assessment in an intentional way and incorporate it into every lesson. No longer am I satisfied to simply record students' performance on assignments and quizzes; now, my goal is to find out, as I teach, what the students understand and how they think. I am still interested in honing my lessons, but along with planning the sequence of learning activities, I also prepare to question students about their thinking during class discussions, in individual conversations, and on written assignments. In addition, linking assessment with instruction has become a key issue in the professional development I provide to other teachers.

After teaching a lesson, we need to determine whether the lesson was accessible to all students while still challenging to the more capable; what the students learned and still need to know; how we can improve the lesson to make it more effective; and, if necessary, what other lesson we might offer as a better alternative. This continual evaluation of instructional choices is at the heart of improving our teaching practice.

Uncovering the Way Students Think

In my early teaching years, I was a devotee of *discovery learning*, sometimes called *inquiry learning*. This instructional approach involves designing learning activities that help students discover concepts and make sense of facts and principles for themselves, rather than relying on textbooks or teacher explanations. I implemented this approach by asking the class a carefully prepared sequence of questions, in the style of Socrates. If a student's response was correct, I continued to the next question. If a student's response was incorrect, other students would typically raise their hands to disagree, and I'd let a class discussion unfold until someone proposed the correct response. Then I'd continue with the next question. If no students objected to an incorrect response, I'd ask a slightly different question to lead students to the right answer.

Years later, I thought about why the discovery method of instruction seemed flawed. The problem was that when a student gave a correct response, I assumed that both the student who had answered correctly and his or her classmates understood the mathematics behind the problem. I never probed students' level of understanding behind their responses; I just happily continued on my teaching trajectory. As a result, I never really knew what students were thinking or whether their correct answers masked incorrect ideas. I only knew that they had given the answer I sought.

I no longer teach this way. Although I still believe in the value and importance of using questions to present ideas for students to consider, I've broadened my use of both oral and written questions so that I now attempt to probe as well as stimulate students' thinking.

For example, when teaching fractions to a class of fourth graders, I wrote five fractions on the board— $\frac{1}{4}$, $\frac{11}{16}$, $\frac{3}{8}$, $\frac{1}{16}$, and $\frac{3}{4}$ —and asked the students to write the fractions in order from smallest to largest. I then added another step by asking them to record their reasons for how they ordered the fractions. After giving the students time to solve the problem, I initiated a whole-class discussion. Robert reported first. He said with confidence, "The smallest fraction is $\frac{1}{16}$." In my early days of teaching, I was accustomed to questioning students when their answers were incorrect, but not when they were correct. Now, however, I asked Robert to explain how he knew that $\frac{1}{16}$ was the smallest fraction. Robert read from his paper, again with confidence, "Because $\frac{1}{16}$ is the lowest number in fractions." The students had previously cut and labeled strips of construction paper to make fraction kits, and $\frac{1}{16}$ happened to be the smallest piece in their kits. The fraction kit—a standard tool in my instructional repertoire that I've always found effective for developing students' understanding of fractions—had led Robert to an incorrect generalization.

By questioning Robert's correct response, I was able not only to clear up his misunderstanding but also to improve on the fraction kit lesson to avoid this problem in the future. When I teach this lesson now, I always ask students to consider how we

would name pieces that are smaller than $\frac{1}{16}$; I talk with them about how we could continue to cut smaller and smaller pieces and find fraction names for even the teeniest sliver.

Incorporating students' reasoning into both written assignments and classroom discussions was a crucial step toward making assessment an integral and ongoing aspect of my classroom instruction. Now it's a staple of my math teaching.

Assessment Through Students' Written Work

One of the main strategies I use to assess students' learning is incorporating writing in math assignments. There are many ways to present writing assignments that yield as much information as possible about what students are thinking (see Burns, 2004).

Ask for more than one strategy. Solving math problems often requires making false starts and searching for new approaches. Students need to develop multiple strategies so that they become flexible in their mathematical thinking and are able to look at mathematical situations from different perspectives. Even when students are performing routine computations, asking them to offer more than one way to arrive at an answer provides insight into their thinking.

For example, I worked with one second grade class that had been focusing on basic addition. When they encountered more difficult problems—those involving numbers above 5, such as $9 + 6$ and $7 + 8$—the students' fallback strategy was always counting. Over time, I helped them develop other strategies for addition. One day, to assess their progress, I asked them to add $6 + 7$ and to explain how they could figure out the answer in more than one way. Their work was revealing. Daniel described five methods, including the following method, that showed the progress he had made with the important skill of *decomposing* numbers—taking numbers apart and combining them in different ways:

> *You take 1 from the 6 and 2 from the 7 and then you add 5 + 5. Then you add on the 1 and the 2 and you get 13.*

Ryan, in contrast, was able to offer only two methods, even when I pushed him for more. He wrote,

> *(1) You start with the 6 and count on 7 more. (2) You start with the 7 and count on 6.*

Although Ryan's work showed that he understood that addition was commutative, it also showed that his addition strategies were limited to counting.

Let students set parameters. A good technique for assessing students' understanding as well as differentiating instruction is to make an assignment adjustable in some way, so that it is accessible and appropriate for a wider range of students. For example, I worked with one 3rd grade class in writing word problems. For several days, the students discussed examples as a group and completed individual assignments. Sometimes I gave a multiplication problem—3 × 4, for example—and asked students to find the answer and also write a word problem around the problem. At other times I gave them a word problem—such as, "How many wheels are there altogether on seven tricycles?"—and asked them to write the related multiplication problem and find the answer. Finally, I gave students the assignment of choosing any multiplication problem, writing a word problem for it, and finding the answer in at least two ways.

Having the students choose their own problems allowed them to decide on the parameters that were comfortable for them. Carrie chose 5 × 2 and wrote a problem about how many mittens five children had. Thomas chose 102 × 4 and wrote a problem about the number of wheels on 102 cars. Each student's choice gave me information about their numerical comfort as well as their skill with multiplication.

Assess the same concept or skill in different ways. I've often found that a student's beginning understanding, although fragile, can provide a useful building block or connection to more robust learning. Sometimes a familiar context can help a student think about a numerically challenging problem. Using flexible assessment approaches enables us to build on students' strengths and interests and help them move on from there.

In a 4th grade class, I watched Josh, who was fascinated by trucks, overcome his confusion about dividing 96 by 8 when I asked him to figure out how many toy 8-wheeler trucks he could make if he had 96 toy wheels. Although his numerical skills were weak, he was able to make progress by drawing trucks and examining the pattern of how many wheels he needed for two trucks, then three trucks, and so on.

Take occasional class inventories. Compiling an inventory for a set of papers can provide a sense of the class's progress and thus inform decisions about how to differentiate instruction. For example, after asking a class of 27 fifth graders to circle the larger fraction—$\frac{2}{3}$ or $\frac{3}{4}$—and explain their reasoning, I reviewed their papers and listed the strategies they used. Their strategies included drawing pictures (either circles or rectangles); changing to fractions with common denominators ($\frac{8}{12}$ and $\frac{9}{12}$); seeing which fraction was closer to 1 ($\frac{2}{3}$ is $\frac{1}{3}$ away, but $\frac{3}{4}$ is only $\frac{1}{4}$ away); and relating the fractions to money ($\frac{2}{3}$ of $1.00 is about 66 cents, whereas $\frac{3}{4}$ of $1.00 is 75 cents). Four of the students were unable to compare the two fractions correctly. I now had direction for future lessons that would provide interventions for the struggling students and give all the students opportunities to learn different strategies from one another.

Assessment Through Classroom Discussion

Incorporating assessment into classroom discussion serves two goals: It provides insights into students' thinking, and it ensures that no student is invisible in the class, but that all are participating and working to understand and learn. Here are some strategies to get the most out of class discussions.

Ask students to explain their answers, whether or not the answers are correct. When I follow up on both correct and incorrect answers by asking students to explain their reasoning, their responses often surprise me. Some students arrive at correct answers in unexpected ways. For example, when comparing $\frac{4}{5}$ and $\frac{3}{4}$, Brandon changed the fractions so that they had common numerators— $\frac{12}{15}$ and $\frac{12}{16}$. He knew that 16ths were smaller than 15ths, so $\frac{12}{15}$, or $\frac{4}{5}$, had to be larger! Students may also surprise us by using incorrect reasoning to arrive at the correct answer. Lindsay, a third grader, used $7 \times 3 = 21$ to conclude that $8 \times 4 = 32$. "Each number is just one bigger," she said, and went on to explain that 1 more than 7 is 8, 1 more than 3 is 4, and 1 more than each of the digits in 21 makes the number 32. Although Lindsay's method worked for this problem, it doesn't work for all problems!

Ask students to share their solution strategies with the group. After a student responds to a question that I pose and explains his or her reasoning, I ask the group, "Who has a different way to solve the problem?" or, "Who has another way to think about this?" I make sure to provide sufficient wait time to encourage students to share ideas. In addition to providing insights into students' thinking and understanding, this method reinforces the idea that there are different ways to think about problems and lets the students know that I value their individual approaches.

Call on students who don't volunteer. For many years, I called only on students who had the confidence to offer their ideas. For students who were less confident, I relied on their written work. I didn't want to intrude on shy students and put them under additional stress. I've since changed this practice, partly because of the insights I gained from the excellent professional resource *Classroom Discussions* (Chapin, O'Connor, & Anderson, 2003). I now tell students that it's important for me to learn about how each of them thinks and, for that reason, I need to hear from all of them. I reassure them, however, that if I call on them and they don't know the answer, they should just let me know. I tell them, "It's important for me to know when a student isn't able to explain so I can think about what kind of support to give." I'm always careful to check in with the student later to determine what kind of intervention I need to provide.

Use small-group work. This technique is especially useful for drawing out students who are reticent about talking in front of the whole class. After posing a problem, I'll often say, "Turn and talk with your partner" or "Talk with your group about this." Then I eavesdrop, paying especially close attention to the students who don't typically talk in class discussions.

Ask students to restate others' ideas. This is another strategy I learned from *Classroom Discussions*. After a student offers an idea or answer, I call on someone else with the prompt, "Explain what Claudia said in your own words." If the student can't do this, I prompt him or her to ask Claudia to explain again. If the student still isn't able to restate Claudia's idea, I ask another student to try, reminding the first student to listen carefully and see whether this alternate explanation helps. After a student shares, I ask Claudia, "Does that describe your idea?" Depending on my professional judgment about the student and the situation, I may also return to the first student and ask him or her to try again.

Improving Mathematics Teaching

According to the National Council of Teachers of Mathematics (2000),

> *To ensure deep, high-quality learning for all students, assessment and instruction must be integrated so that assessment becomes a routine part of the ongoing classroom activity rather than an interruption. Such assessment also provides the information teachers need to make appropriate instructional decisions.*

Making assessment an integral part of daily mathematics instruction is a challenge. It requires planning specific ways to use assignments and discussions to discover what students do and do not understand. It also requires teachers to be prepared to deal with students' responses. Merely spotting when students are incorrect is relatively easy compared with understanding the reasons behind their errors. The latter demands careful attention and a deep knowledge of the mathematics concepts and principles that students are learning.

But the benefits are worth the effort. By building and using a wide repertoire of assessment strategies, we can get to know more about our students than we ever thought possible. The insights we gain by making assessment a regular part of instruction enable us to meet the needs of the students who are eager for more challenges and to provide intervention for those who are struggling.

References

Burns, M. (2004). "Writing in math." *Educational Leadership*, 62(2), 30–33.

Chapin, S. H., O'Connor, C., & Anderson, N. C. (2003). *Classroom discussions: Using math talk to help students learn*. Sausalito, CA: Math Solutions Publications.

National Council of Teachers of Mathematics. (2000). *Principles and standards for school mathematics*. Reston, VA: Author. Available: http://standards.nctm.org

Marilyn Burns is founder of Math Solutions Professional Development, Sausalito, California; 800-868-9092; mburns@mathsolutions.com.

Marilyn Burns On the Language of Math

Parlez-vous geometry? Sprechen sie fractions? An expert's guide to teaching math's unique vocabulary.

Math can sometimes seem like a strange language from a foreign land—one communicated in symbols, numbers, and geometric figures. And when we talk about mathematical concepts, even familiar, garden-variety words—such as *parallel*, *power*, *even*, *odd*, *multiply*, *difference*, *product*, *positive*, and *negative*—take on brand-new meanings.

What's the best way for teachers to help students master this unique vocabulary? In 2000, after analyzing two decades of research on vocabulary instruction, the National Reading Panel concluded that there is no one best method for teaching vocabulary. Rather, teachers need to use a variety of methods for the best results, including intentional, explicit instruction of specific vocabulary words.

With this in mind, we asked Marilyn Burns, founder of Math Solutions Professional Development and a frequent contributor to *Instructor*, how teachers can effectively integrate math vocabulary into their lesson plans.

Q: *How is math like another language?*

A: The meanings of words in general usage are often very different from their mathematical meanings. Take *even*, for example: In common usage we talk about shares being even when each person has the same amount, or knitting stitches being even when they are consistently the same size, or a person having an even disposition, or getting even when we feel we've been wronged. This is further complicated in the context of mathematics where we use *even* to describe a whole number divisible by 2, which means it can be divided (or shared, if you like) into two equal groups with nothing remaining, or a remainder of zero.

Even is just one example. In common usage, *meter* can refer to a poetic rhythm or to a device, like a water meter, that measures flow; in mathematics, *meter* is a unit of length. In common usage, when we talk about things that *multiply*, such as animals or plants, we mean that they increase in number; when we *multiply* numbers in mathematics, however, we specifically mean that we are combining a certain number of equal size groups, which we often describe as repeated addition. And while the quantities always increase in real-world contexts when things multiply, in the world of mathematics, when we multiply fractions, the answer is often less than one or both of the numbers we multiply!

Q: *Should we teach math the way we teach a second language?*

A: It's not exactly analogous to learning a foreign language. When studying Spanish, I learned new words for naming things, asking questions, describing my thoughts, and so on. But I already had knowledge about the ideas I wanted to express, and learning Spanish was all about learning a new language for communicating these ideas.

In contrast, the purpose of the language of mathematics is communicating about mathematical ideas, and it's necessary first to acquire knowledge about the ideas that the mathematical language describes. Only when I understand mathematical ideas do I have a reason for learning the correct language of mathematics to communicate about these ideas.

Q: *What's the best way to teach both ideas and vocabulary?*

A: Mathematical vocabulary and also mathematical symbols are determined by social conventions. For example, it's not possible to figure out through reasoning that the numbers we multiply are called *factors*—this is an arbitrary, agreed-upon convention. In contrast, mathematical ideas have their foundation in logic. The source of the knowledge lies inside the learner.

For both types of knowledge—social and logical—explicit instruction is essential. However, the character of the instruction vastly differs. For teaching social knowledge, we must provide the information to the learner—through explanations or through access to another source of information. There's no way to figure out on our own that numbers that aren't divisible by 2 are called odd numbers, for example.

However, knowing if a specific number is or isn't divisible by 2 calls for mathematical knowledge that we gain by synthesizing what we know about division, and connecting this understanding with what we know about patterns of numbers. Teachers must first make sense of these concepts themselves, then use appropriate instruction that helps kids make their own sense of the concepts.

Q: *Give us an example of teaching a math concept followed by the relevant vocabulary.*

A: To help young children develop understanding about even and odd numbers, I use an activity called Two-Hand Take Away.

First give each child seven objects, such as cubes, and have each child place them in a row. Then, using both hands, the children take one away from each end of the row. Verify with them that now there are only five cubes in the row. Have them do this again, leaving three, and once more, leaving only one cube. Now they're done because it's not possible to do another two-hand take away. Now repeat the activity with eight objects; this time they wind up with no cubes left over.

Have children keep track of what happens by writing the numbers of cubes they start with in one of two columns: "Zero Left Over" or "One Left Over."

After they record the activity using seven and eight objects, they can try again using other numbers of their choice. Encourage students to predict each time.

After many trials, give each child a 1-to-100 chart titled "Zero Left Over." (List 1 through 10 across the top, 11 through 20 underneath it, 21 through 30 underneath that, and so on.) Ask kids to color in all the numbers with zero left over. Now talk about the pattern, both on the chart (colored-in numbers are all in the same columns) and by looking at the digits in the ones places (which are always 0, 2, 4, 6, or 8). After children can predict what will happen for any number of objects when they do Two-Hand Take Away, they're ready to learn the mathematical language: that those numbers with zero left over are *even* and those with one left over are *odd*.

Q: *What other strategies are best for teaching math vocabulary?*

A: First, identify the vocabulary to be taught. It's important to determine the relevant terminology for each unit of study and for daily lessons. Introduce the vocabulary only after developing understanding of the related mathematical ideas, connecting its meaning to the students' learning experiences.

Write new vocabulary on a class chart. Seeing words written is supportive for all students and essential for some. Have students keep their own lists. Copying words from the chart will give students a first experience with writing them down, and they can use these lists for at-home assignments.

When vocabulary relates to mathematical symbols, point to the symbols when saying the words. Have the students pronounce the words themselves.

Encourage students to use the vocabulary in discussions and on assignments, and use it repeatedly and consistently yourself. Prompt students to use new terminology when they present ideas or complete assignments. For older students, introduce words with multiple meanings, and have kids define them.

POLYGON POWER: FROM CONCEPTS TO VOCAB

Building on their prior knowledge of geometry, Marilyn Burns teaches Danielle Ross's fifth-grade class at Park School in Mill Valley, California, how to define and classify polygons.

STEP 1: I drew a vertical line to divide the board into two columns and placed two shapes drawn on cards in each column. I didn't label the columns yet, but planned later to label the left column "Polygons" and the right column "Not Polygons."

STEP 2: I held up four more shapes, and students voted as to which column they should go in. I then told them where each shape belonged and placed it there.

STEP 3: I asked students to think quietly about what they thought was my classification system. Then, in pairs, they talked about their ideas and drew a shape they would like to add to the chart.

STEP 4: Next, students shared their drawings, and we worked together to sort them correctly on the chart.

STEP 5: I labeled the columns "Polygons" and "Not Polygons." I asked what they thought were the characteristics of the shapes that were polygons, and I wrote their ideas on the board. Together, we wrote a definition of *polygon*.

STEP 6: Finally, I used the shapes posted to introduce or reinforce additional vocabulary related to polygons: *triangle, quadrilateral, square, parallelogram, rhombus, rectangle, pentagon*, and so on.

Reflecting on Math Instruction

After reading the professional articles, reflect on your own teaching practices.

Looking at How Students Reason (pages 83–87)

1. How do you currently use assessment to inform your instruction?

_____

_____

2. Why is the ongoing integration of assessment and instruction important?

_____

_____

3. How can you use student writing to assess understanding and inform instruction?

_____

_____

4. In what ways can you use class discussions to assess student understanding and inform instruction?

_____

_____

Marilyn Burns On the Language of Math (pages 88–90)

1. What role does explicit vocabulary instruction currently have in your classroom?

_____

_____

2. In what ways is vocabulary instruction important when teaching math?

_____

_____

3. What are the benefits of teaching math vocabulary after students have experienced the math concept?

_____

_____

Do The Math Glossary

Below are definitions of recurring words and phrases used throughout the *Do The Math* program. For definitions of content-specific math vocabulary terms, refer to your *Do The Math* Teacher Guide.

Assessment and Differentiation

One of eight proven instructional strategies, ongoing assessment is integrated throughout the *Do The Math* program in the form of teacher observation and evaluation of student work and interactions. A progress monitoring assessment occurs every fifth lesson to help teachers identify those students who need additional support and those students who are ready for a greater challenge.

Beginning-of-Module Assessment

A summative assessment located in the back of each Teacher Guide and on the *TeacherSpace* CD-ROM that is given before teaching a *Do The Math* module. Use the results to verify appropriate student placement and record these baseline scores for comparison with the End-of-Module Assessment results.

Community News

A flyer distributed at the beginning of every fifth lesson to communicate with the families of students participating in the *Do The Math* program. Located in the back of each Teacher Guide and available in Spanish and English on the *TeacherSpace* CD-ROM, the flyer summarizes the content covered in the five lessons and suggests a math activity for practicing the math concepts at home.

End-of-Module Assessment

A summative assessment located in the back of each Teacher Guide and on the *TeacherSpace* CD-ROM that is given after students complete a *Do The Math* module. The results help determine student readiness for the next module and measure student growth when compared with the results of the Beginning-of-Module Assessment.

Explicit Instruction

One of eight proven instructional strategies embedded in the *Do The Math* program that requires teachers to guide students in recognizing relationships between mathematical concepts and connecting newly acquired concepts to previous math experiences.

Games

Math-related, high-interest activities integrated into each module to provide practice with key math concepts and skills. A clearly labeled red mesh bag provides convenient storage for all the games materials needed to serve up to eight students.

Gradual Release

A four-phase pedagogy that gradually releases students from teacher guidance as they learn to apply math skills independently. Gradual release is one of eight proven instructional strategies embedded in the *Do The Math* program.

Manipulatives

Hands-on materials that visually represent abstract math concepts are incorporated throughout *Do The Math* to provide students concrete experiences with abstract ideas.

Math Solutions Professional Development

An organization, founded in 1984 by Marilyn Burns, dedicated to improving math instruction by providing professional development services to teachers and administrators in grades K–8.

Meaningful Practice

Repeated practice and application of newly acquired math skills. One of eight proven instructional strategies, practice is an essential part of every *Do The Math* lesson—in partner work, written practice in the *WorkSpace*, and interactive games that reinforce math skills.

Module

A unit of study with a specific area of focus. *Do The Math* is organized into 12 modules; each one includes summative assessments and a series of 30 step-by-step lessons. Each module is designed to be taught in 30-minute classes, five days a week.

Multiple Strategies

One of eight proven instructional strategies embedded in the *Do The Math* program that deepens student understanding of math by engaging students in learning new concepts in multiple ways, with games, read alouds, and manipulatives.

Objectives Tracker

A record-keeping chart located in the back of each Teacher Guide and on the *TeacherSpace* CD-ROM to track student progress in meeting the objectives for the module.

Progress Monitoring

Occurs every fifth lesson of a *Do The Math* module. Students independently complete a Show What You Know page in the *WorkSpace*. Teachers use the information to track student progress and differentiate instruction to address student needs.

Read Alouds

Children's literature that is incorporated into the lessons to provide a context for math instruction. Each module includes two copies of the read aloud(s)—one for the classroom library and one for the teacher to use during classroom instruction.

Scaffolded Content

One of eight proven instructional strategies embedded in the *Do The Math* program that involves breaking challenging tasks or skills into smaller, more manageable steps that are then sequenced and paced to support students' understanding.

Show What You Know

WorkSpace pages appearing every fifth lesson that students complete independently and teachers use to monitor student progress and differentiate instruction.

Student Interaction

One of eight proven instructional strategies embedded in the *Do The Math* program, where students work together in a whole group, a small group, or in pairs to solve problems, play games, clarify their thinking, and explain their reasoning.

Student Pair Materials

A clearly labeled red mesh bag that conveniently stores all the hands-on materials student pairs require throughout the *Do The Math* program. Each module comes with four bags to serve eight students.

Survey

An informal student self-assessment located in the back of the Teacher Guide and on the *TeacherSpace* CD-ROM that provides information about the students' disposition toward math before and after completing a *Do The Math* module.

Teacher Bookcase

A box that stores all teacher materials and professional resources needed to successfully implement the *Do The Math* module, including the Teacher Guide, *TeacherSpace™*, *Annotated WorkSpace*, *Teaching Arithmetic* book, read-aloud book(s), and Teacher Demonstration Materials.

Teacher Demonstration Materials

A clearly labeled red mesh bag that provides convenient storage and access to all the teacher materials needed for each lesson's instruction.

Teacher Guide

The primary teacher resource for the *Do The Math* program, providing all the information teachers need to teach the lessons, monitor student progress, and effectively use all program materials.

TeacherSpace™

A binder included in the Teacher Bookcase that organizes all professional resources and includes a CD-ROM with videos, reproducibles, and professional articles.

Teaching Arithmetic

A professional resource from Math Solutions Publications included in the Teacher Bookcase to provide additional mathematical and pedagogical support.

Think, Pair, Share

A nonthreatening approach to engaging students in discussion of a math concept. Students think on their own, discuss their ideas with a partner, then share their ideas with the whole group. Think, Pair, Share is a student interaction strategy embedded throughout the *Do The Math* program.

Vocabulary and Language

An essential part of every *Do The Math* lesson and one of eight instructional strategies embedded in the program. Vocabulary is taught after students engage in the math concept using a consistent routine—students see the word, hear the teacher say it, say the word themselves, write it in their *WorkSpace*, and read the glossary definitions. Each lesson also contains Spanish translations of key terms, providing additional language support for Spanish-speaking students.

WorkSpace

Consumable books used by students to practice the math concepts learned throughout the *Do The Math* module and to demonstrate their progress toward meeting objectives for the module.

Do The Math®

Implementation Training
Evaluation

Name (optional) _____ Date _____

School/District _____

Trainer _____

Circle the topic(s) you learned about in this training:

Addition & Subtraction   Multiplication   Division   Fractions

Please answer the following questions by circling the number, with 1 as lowest and 5 as highest.

1. Overall, how satisfied were you with this training?   **1 2 3 4 5**

2. To what extent did the content meet its stated objectives?   **1 2 3 4 5**

3. How satisfied were you with (rate all that apply to your training):

    a. Welcome and Program Background   **1 2 3 4 5**

    b. Materials Overview   **1 2 3 4 5**

    c. *Do The Math* Model Lesson   **1 2 3 4 5**

    d. Teaching With *Do The Math*   **1 2 3 4 5**

    e. Assessing and Differentiating Instruction   **1 2 3 4 5**

    f. Implementing *Do The Math*   **1 2 3 4 5**

    g. Ongoing Professional Development   **1 2 3 4 5**

What recommendations do you have for future *Do The Math* trainings?

_____

_____

_____

What questions do you still have?

_____

_____

_____